Everyone asks you how the baby is. Are they well? Can they come see them? How are they sleeping? Eating? But they don't often stop and ask how you are. Are you managing to eat? Are you managing to sleep? Are you coping OK?

brazen

Praise for *GROW:*

OPEN is an intimate, honest and powerful read.
So personal you want to jump into the pages.
–Giovanna Fletcher

Intensely moving but also full of practical advice.
–Alastair Campbell

A beautiful read.
–Zoe Ball

GROW

FRANKIE BRIDGE

WITH CONTRIBUTIONS FROM
DR ED ABRAHAMSON (PAEDIATRICIAN)
MALEHA KHAN (CLINICAL PSYCHOLOGIST)

brazen

AUGUST 2021
FIRST EDITION

First published in Great Britain in 2021
by Brazen, an imprint of
Octopus Publishing Group Ltd
Carmelite House
50 Victoria Embankment
London EC4Y 0DZ
www.octopusbooks.co.uk

An Hachette UK Company
www.hachette.co.uk

Layout and design copyright
© Octopus Publishing Group 2021
Text Copyright © Frankie Bridge 2021

ISBN 978 1 91424 002 7

A CIP catalogue record for this book
is available from the British Library

Printed and bound in the UK

10 9 8 7 6 5 4 3 2

This FSC® label means that materials
used for the product have been
responsibly sourced

MIX
Paper from
responsible sources
FSC® C104740

This book is dedicated
to Parker and Carter

ABOUT THE AUTHOR

Frankie Bridge is best known as one-fifth of The Saturdays and outside of music, she has established herself as a TV presenter and digital influencer. Frankie became an ambassador for Mind after opening up about her experiences of anxiety, depression and panic attacks after her hospitalization in May 2012. Having initially dealt with these issues in silence, she has been keen to support Mind in making sure that no one has to face a mental health problem alone. Recently, Frankie has been a key player in helping to launch the Mind partnership with the mental health initiative Heads Together, as well as lending her support to Time to Talk Day. In 2019, she launched her first podcast series, OPEN MIND, focusing on mental health. It debuted in the top ten podcasts upon release. In 2020, she published OPEN, which went on to become a *Sunday Times* bestseller.

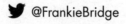 @FrankieBridge

@FrankieBridge

CONTENTS

Introduction

Dear You

This little life you have brought into the world is your everything.

And your world in that instant **changed for ever.**

We can grow a whole new human being inside our bellies, and our skin, muscles and organs all move around to allocate the correct space needed for them to keep on growing inside us. For the majority of us, we don't even have to think about it or do anything for it to happen. It just does, the body just knows what to do! It's completely magical. But for me, that's the only magical, unknowing part of the whole thing, the rest we have to learn along the way. Both mum and baby learn from each other. As soon as the baby we have grown inside us is outside us, we have to help them to grow. We have to teach them how to grow up and release them into the world.

And this requires us to grow as mothers too.

We have to learn how to do this as we go along and what they need from us as they start to realize who they are. Don't get me wrong, this can be magical, but it can also be hard, at times terrifying, and your body and mind will be changed by it for ever. No matter what happens, once they are born you will always, constantly think of them. They become something bigger than you and the rest of the world. They become your life's work, the world shrinks down to this one tiny human.

But here's the thing, it sometimes comes at a cost. A cost that no one ever really talks about. The cost of giving them everything they need to grow can often mean that you and your mental health fall to the wayside. We neglect our wants and needs and those around us do too. For a long time after, everyone asks you how the baby is. Are they well? Can they come see them? How are they sleeping? Eating? But they don't often stop and ask how you are. Are you managing to eat and drink? Are you managing to sleep? Are you coping OK?

It can often feel like you're alone in this thing called motherhood, that you're the only one struggling or not loving every single second and that you're never going to have another hot cup of tea or dinner for the rest of your life. The truth is, we all struggle with our mental health at times, at any stage of motherhood, no matter how young or old our kids are. Never really feeling like we have all the answers. And feeling like our wants and our needs are no longer important, to us or anyone else.

What I instead learned was that . . . My child would *always* be on my mind: no matter where I was or what I was doing, he would be there for the rest of my life. And while of course that's not necessarily a bad thing, the realization can certainly be overwhelming and scary. I had so little control over this whole new part of my mind that would forever worry about and care for him. My career had been my main focus for most of my life, but now, how would I be able to commit the time and focus I needed to do both things? Something that I think so many women feel, but also are too afraid to say out loud, for fear of sounding ungrateful or unable to cope with their new life ahead. It was a realization, not a regret, that my life was never going to be the same again. Which was in so many ways a change from my usual anxieties that had consumed so much of my life and mind, but it was also terrifying and totally unexpected. I felt out of control of who I had become and who I was becoming.

The problem is that as women we are told we can have it all.

That we should want it all.

And we can do it all.

We are sold the dream from a young age that we should be successful, find love, have children, devote ourselves completely to our family and also stay successful – and then our lives will be complete.

Tick all the boxes:
for mother
woman
life.

And of course, there are women who achieve this. But for most of us, if anything falls out of that perfect list, we believe (or have been taught to feel as if) we have failed at being a woman. It's this belief or this sense of failure that results in none of us embracing so much of the mess that is part of growing up as a parent or as a person. Because mistakes are no longer something to be made and then learned from, they are something to be held against us by others – but let's be honest, mainly by ourselves. We often feel that if we don't have a huge smile plastered across our faces, or aren't posting on social media about how much we love every single second of it all, then . . . we are *ungrateful* and *bad mothers*. How did we get so removed from how we actually feel and how did we ever think this would make us better parents? Better mothers? Or happy humans?

Remember, this book is all from **my** experience of motherhood, yours might be very different from mine. And guess what? **Neither of us is right or wrong**. We need to get to a point in society where neither journey is judged. A lot of this book is about us learning to grow into who we are, not mourning our former selves. And as women, I don't think this is taught to us or spoken about enough. The onus being that we have to have children, but not look or act like we do. From the moment we realize we are pregnant, we have to 'carry' a child everywhere we go, both physically and mentally, and when they are born we have to carry them into and through the world. This involves sacrifice and it involves giving over a part of ourselves in order to help create something else. Accepting this is an integral part of growing a child, but also growing as a person and as a mother.

Welcome to GROW.

Frankie
x

We're going to be joined by two people who have helped me a great deal on this journey: my psychologist, Maleha Khan, and Dr Ed Abrahamson, consultant paediatrician at the Cromwell Hospital, London and vice-president of the Cornwall Air Ambulance. Paediatricians specialize in the medical care of infants and children, while clinical psychologists specialize in the diagnosis and psychological treatment of mental, behavioural and emotional illnesses. They do not prescribe medications but use a range of techniques such as Cognitive Behavioural Therapy (CBT). Comments from Maleha and Dr Ed are marked with the symbols below:

MALEHA KHAN
psychologist

DR ED ABRAHAMSON
paediatrician

BECOMING A NEW PARENT

 There is no doubt that the joy of becoming a new parent can be overwhelming – your life changes overnight. It is a seismic shock, yet all the expectations of society and the extended family are that you are going be unconditionally elated.

After delivery, the most commonly heard phrase is 'Mother and baby are both doing well.' But has anyone asked the mother what she really feels? They never say, 'Baby is doing well but mother is wrecked – 12 hours in labour, a third-degree vaginal tear, eight stitches and she can't even pee now as she is in so much pain.' The presumption that the mother will cope with everything nature throws at her starts here. It is a narrative that may continue right through the early months and years – often the mother won't get her first sign of sympathy until her cute baby has grown into a screaming, demonic toddler.

Society presumes a newborn baby induces a nirvana-like state in its parents, who have arrived at their utopian destination. It often is like this, but not always. Inside there can be many conflicting emotions and the pressure to be outwardly ecstatic only adds to the guilt that you may feel for not being over the moon. Indeed, I have looked after many new parents where it has been the dad who has struggled, and there is a lack of awareness and understanding of this phenomenon. Perhaps one of the last taboo subjects – paternal post-natal depression.

Having your first baby is probably the most challenging life event you will face, other than serious illness or the death of a loved one.

Having your first baby is probably the most challenging life event you will face, other than serious illness or the death of a loved one. Every parent will react differently to a new baby at home. If there are two parents, they can sometimes be on a completely different page in terms of their approaches and feelings.

The role of the health professionals that are almost always involved with newborn babies, including midwives, health visitors, GPs, practice nurses and then in some cases paediatricians, is to have their antennae well positioned to detect the signals and intervene to support the family. Time pressures and, in 2020 and 2021, the lack of face-to-face contact and home visits caused by the COVID-19 pandemic, may contribute to signs being missed, and therefore parental and, as a consequence, infant needs not being met.

The awareness of the potential emotional impact is crucial, as this can have a direct bearing on the early weeks and months of the new baby's life. If you feel stress and anxiety, this may well result in an unhappy early experience for everyone, and indeed lead to symptoms in the baby which may be misconstrued as a sign of ill health.

The two most common manifestations are constant crying and poor feeding, which can lead to attendance at the GP or paediatrician's office, followed by a whole series of often unnecessary interventions. For example, it is not unusual for a healthy baby to end up on several medications and special hypoallergenic milks and for new mothers to be asked to restrict their diet or stop breast feeding altogether, when there may be nothing physically wrong.

In my 25 years as a consultant paediatrician, I consider the single most consistent and greatest failing of the whole support system for new (particularly first-time) parents to be a lack of time – the time to listen, time to talk and time to help them take those baby steps, literally and metaphorically, on the often-challenging journey ahead. For anxious new mums like Frankie, whose past medical history and mental-health issues should be known to her medical practitioners, even greater emphasis on talking and listening is needed.

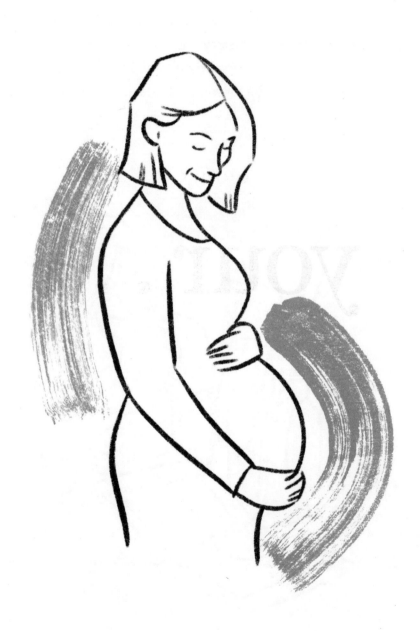

CHAPTER ONE

your . . .

YOUR BODY NO LONGER BELONGS TO YOU

Although we know that all pregnancies are different, we can't help but believe in and aspire to having the perfect pregnancy we are sold by the world.

The glowing mother-to-be
with shiny hair and perfect skin.
The bump that appears while the rest of
your body stays exactly the same.
Full of joy and fertility.
Once the baby is out, the mother's
body quickly goes back to how it was
(before it stretched to accommodate
a small elephant).

The myth that nothing in life changes and you live happily ever after.
That you are going to LOVE every step.
Being a 'natural' mother.

Well, I am sorry to tell you, this is a big old lie (for most of us). The utter scam of motherhood. False advertising. Social-media untruths.

Your body has just performed the most miraculous thing it will probably ever do, creating life, and will *never* go back to how it once was, which is part of the beauty of life and of the female body.

Female octopuses sacrifice their lives to give birth in order to give their offspring all their bodily goodness. There has always been sacrifice in creating life as you have to give it a part of yours. We also give a huge amount to create our children, though the world doesn't want to sell that to us new mums.

But we sell this to each other, too.

How she is doing so well.

How easy it all was for her.

How fantastic her life is.

How her jeans fit.

How perfectly perfect she is.

And, yes, this is the truth for some women,
but they are the *exception*, not the *rule*.

Big or small, bounce back or not,
a natural mother or someone who
struggles, one that has to learn that
neither is right or wrong.

Neither is normal or abnormal.

No-one should feel ashamed of their
body or made to feel bad for their
journey. We are all different and that's
what makes it interesting.

We should normalize not feeling normal.

Because something very **big**
has happened to us!

On the one hand, I felt immense pride in the fact that my body was growing another human. It truly is something magical and amazing. I was so proud to be carrying a baby that was part me and part my husband, Wayne. That we were adding to our family and we had no idea how this little one was going to turn out or what kind of person they would be felt exciting and nothing short of miraculous. On the other hand, I also carried the immense weight of underlying shame – quite literally. I was so ashamed and, if I'm honest, so shocked that I wasn't a gorgeous, glowing, neat and tidy pregnant woman. Indeed, my bum was bigger than my bump most of the time, my ankles were so full of water by three months that I no longer had ankles, and people often thought I was carrying twins. All of which was made worse by the fact that I was in the public eye.

I felt like I had failed at pregnancy. That I already wasn't the 'right kind' of mother.

I felt like I had failed at pregnancy. That I already wasn't the 'right kind' of mother.

The thing is, I've never been someone who had a good relationship with their body. I've always felt like the only way I can look 'good' (and by that I mean thin) is to suffer and punish myself. From a young age, I came to believe that my beauty was the only power I had. While never really feeling or believing I was actually beautiful. Does that make sense to you? After years of counselling, I still haven't understood it either. My looks got me things that I wanted but never believed I deserved to have. I felt that my body was my only asset. So I began to restrict my food intake, feeling worthy and excited if my bones were jutting out and believing that going to bed hungry was a huge accomplishment. If someone said I looked a little too thin, it only encouraged me further, but looking back, I see how disordered my eating had become and how much I exerted control over myself through starving myself.

It wasn't until I was pregnant for the first time that I truly experienced being out of control of my own body. And while for some that's part of the journey, to see what their body can do, it terrified me. It was as though my body was paying me back for all the time I spent punishing it. Minus the morning sickness, the uncontrollable change in my physical appearance made me unable to enjoy my pregnancy.

Two of the biggest changes in my body that I was not told about or hadn't expected were the size and colour of my nipples. Why did I not know about this? And would they ever return to normal? They were so large, I swear it looked like they were eating the rest of my boob! And they became very bumpy, too – I found out it's to lubricate your nipples and alert your baby when it's time to feed.

The second surprise was the size of my vulva in the third trimester. I literally remember being in the shower and screaming out, 'What the hell is happening? Why is it so big?' Now it makes total sense: with the amount of pressure that was being pushed onto it from the baby, of course it was swollen. But at the time I found it terrifying and, again, no one had forewarned me of any changes beyond my growing bellly.

For those of you that haven't been pregnant, or are currently pregnant: all of these things do go back to normal. My nipples are now of average size and colour and my vulva equally so.

 A lot of women do not enjoy pregnancy, but it is still almost a taboo thing to admit. Nothing can prepare you for what happens physically and psychologically.

And yes, my baby was healthy and growing well, which I knew was the only thing that mattered. But the hard truth is, nine months is a long time not to feel like yourself, and let's be honest, for most it's ten months. And that's not including the fourth trimester, which is the 12 weeks after you've had the baby – the time when you go through even more physical and mental changes. And you and your baby get used to life outside of the womb.

The assumed normality of commenting on a pregnant woman's appearance, saying how extraordinary she looks, is pretty close to fetishization. And then we all do it again when we see the same woman after she's had her baby: 'Wow, you look amazing!' As if we're surprised and as though the most important thing for a woman to do after giving birth is to *look good*?

Let me ask that once more:

Why is the first thing we talk about how we look?

There are so many mixed messages when you're pregnant. Everyone has different advice for you and the internet is one of the most confusing places to be when pregnant. For years people have said, 'Eat what you want, you're eating for two.' Now they say, 'Only eat a few more calories than you did before.' But I was starving hungry throughout my pregnancies. My hormones told me to eat. I have the same cravings when I get my periods, so when I was pregnant, it was like that but on steroids. I also got pretty bad morning sickness, and I found that eating stopped me from feeling so nauseous. The only thing I wanted to eat were carbohydrates, and as someone who has a phobia of being sick, I was willing to do anything to make the nausea go away. For both of my pregnancies I had such conflicting emotions.

As women we are made to feel that whatever shape we take, we are not enough.

I hated anyone looking at my pregnant body and felt that everyone was either laughing at me or disgusted by me. I am not proud of this, but it is my truth, and I think that as women we should be able to discuss how hard these changes are for us, our minds and our bodies. We are made to shift into mums overnight and accept our changing bodies, when previously all we have been told by the media is that we should control our weight. As women we are made to feel that whatever shape we take, we are not enough.

I don't have *those* beautiful pre-birth, post-birth pictures. I didn't just snap back and, seven years on, that still hurts. When I was pregnant, although I knew my body was amazing as it was growing a human inside it, truthfully I wanted to hide from the world. I envied the women who you couldn't tell had had a baby unless they were with them, but I also envied the mothers who had the stretch marks, the loose skin, but who were proud of what their bodies had achieved and embraced their new shape.

I still wear all of mine with shame. A mother who overindulged; couldn't control herself around food; took antidepressants during pregnancy, which contributed to the stretch marks all over my body from the water retention brought on by the drugs. They are still a constant reminder that I couldn't even do pregnancy right, something I had longed for from such a young age.

 Frankie realized that her body was not recognizable, the curves and swelling were unfamiliar. Frankie put on four stone during her first pregnancy, a side effect of one of her antidepressants. She was retaining so much water that her body was unrecognizable to her. She began to feel out of control and ashamed of her body. She has spoken in the past about her struggles with an eating disorder.

Still, years on, not a day goes by where I don't feel disappointed in my body and myself for how I treated it while I was pregnant. I don't see my stretch marks and wobbly bits as badges of honour, I feel ashamed of my failings as a person that allowed them. It affects how I dress and how I approach my health and fitness routines. I try to do both as much as possible, but there are times when I just think, what's the point? I could lose a stone, tone up every single muscle, but all those faults will still be there. Those reminders of that time when I lost all control. That time when I let myself down.

Yet the madness here is this: I don't look at any other women and judge them for any of the things I judge myself for, so why is it OK to do it to myself? We are all so guilty of this.

 Frankie's thoughts and feelings of doubts about her abilities trigger a sense of shame. Frankie's impostor syndrome dictates that she has to be perfect at everything, even pregnancy. People who don't have this are OK with not being brilliant at everything.

Many of us were given Barbie dolls to play with when we were younger. I had a Sindy doll when I was a child, which someone gave me for my birthday. She had a bump that you clicked onto her tummy and then when you took it off she had a flat stomach again. That's what I imagined would happen after I had a baby, but of course that wasn't what happened at all. Celebrities who post images of their bodies weeks after giving birth, looking exactly like their previous selves, sell us this narrative too. But that is their truth – maybe they did bounce back, and they shouldn't be made to feel guilty or ashamed of that. But for a while that was all we would see, because women who didn't 'bounce back' have felt too ashamed to share their post-baby bodies. But there has been a big shift in that recently and I welcome it with open arms. No 'body' is wrong, but it's great for us to see all versions. The truth, for me, was that I felt worse after giving birth than when I had the bump. At least when it was a bump, there was a gorgeous little baby living inside me. Now it was just a flabby, loose bit of skin, of no use to anyone. Looking back, I can't believe how naïve I was, but at the time I was devastated and I felt as though my body had let me down. All I wanted was to look and feel like the old me, which is strange because I never really liked or appreciated that version of me either.

Isn't it terrifying how hard we can be on ourselves? I've never looked at a friend and thought, *Oh gosh, she should have lost that baby tum by now.* Yet, two days after giving birth, it seemed totally acceptable to expect that from myself. I mean, give yourself a break, woman! You've just brought a brand-new life into the world and basically been cut in half. But the comedown is hard, from being proud of a bump to being ashamed of what's left of it. Rather than understanding that both these bodies, the pregnant and the post-natal, have achieved the same thing. We are less consumable to society.

We have grown something and because of that, we have changed in the process.

If we always judge mothers on their appearance, then this is always going to be the thing that we learn is the most important. I've certainly said it many times before, but now instead of saying 'Wow, you look amazing!', I stop and say, 'Wow, you look like you're coping really well. Are you doing OK?'

I remember once seeing a mum doing the nursery run. The last time I had seen her was when she had a bump. Now there she was, at the school gates, on time, newborn strapped to her, toddler in tow, in an outfit that matched, no puke in her hair, and, most importantly, she seemed calm. I'd never properly met her before or had a chance to speak to her, but I wanted her to know that someone had noticed that she was doing a great job. So I said, 'Hey, congratulations, good on you, you're doing a great job. I didn't manage to leave the house for weeks!'

I make an effort to say something nice to mothers that isn't based on how they look but on how they are doing.

We know each other better now and, when we talked about it, she remembered me saying this to her and told me that at the time, she didn't feel like she was doing a 'good job' and it had made her feel so much better when I reminded her that, just by leaving the house, she was!

From that moment on, I've always tried to make an effort to say something nice to mothers that isn't based on how they look but on how they are doing (even if I feel shy or embarrassed). A kind observation from a stranger or a friend really does go a long way. Someone else acknowledging that it's tough and you're not alone in how you're feeling right now can be transformative.

Antenatal depression

As someone who has long suffered from depression and anxiety, I was fully ready to be hit with post-natal depression once my baby was here. An educated and carefully thought-out decision was made for me to stay on my antidepressants during both my pregnancies. That's still a controversial issue, but it shouldn't be, as long as it's dealt with by a professional, who knows what they're doing and who is monitoring how much you are taking and when. We are fed this notion that taking antidepressants when pregnant is an absolute no go, and it's just not true these days. Both my babies had to be examined daily after birth for withdrawal symptoms, which admittedly filled me with guilt, but I was there for them and able to be the mum that they needed and deserved because of the antidepressants. Without my medication, that just wouldn't have been possible.

I didn't experience post-natal depression myself, although I know so many women who did. I think it was probably because I was still on my antidepressants, so I had that lifejacket. But my depression was very bad during pregnancy. Imagine how bad things could have been if I hadn't stayed on my medication!

My lowness during pregnancy was the result of an accumulation of things:

the morning sickness
the changes in my body
feeling out of control
all the usual anxieties of pregnancy
anxiety about what the future held.

Most people don't seem to know about or expect antenatal depression, because we've been told this is the happiest time of our lives, right? But perhaps that's why women suffer from it – they're too scared to say they're not enjoying their pregnancy like they thought they would, and they feel as though they are failing their baby before it has even been born – failing to love the process makes them scared that they may not love the child or being a mother. But the state of being pregnant is brief and motherhood is for ever, and the more open we can be about antenatal depression, the more women we can catch before they fall too far.

The expectations of pregnancy are different for us all; but for me it felt like the lowest point and I really struggled with, and fought, the changes happening to me. I thought of being scared of them as a failure, when it was actually antenatal depression. And when you don't understand this, like I didn't, you try to explain the crying as 'just hormones' but the truth is, you're struggling.

Morning sickness

Surely it's time to rename 'morning sickness'? Anyone who's actually had morning sickness will know that it's not just in the morning. It can occur at any time of the day and sometimes all day and all night.

With my first pregnancy, I had standard morning sickness, but was never actually physically sick. Instead I experienced insane levels of nausea with lots of gagging. Sometimes I actually hoped to be sick, just to relieve the nausea symptoms, which lasted a lot longer than 12 weeks. There were times when I'd come home from work sobbing, as having to pretend that you're OK and loving it all day long is exhausting. On top of the pregnancy exhaustion, I never got the second-trimester energy surge either. It just never arrived: I remained flattened throughout.

Now let's talk about **Hyperemesis Gravidarum (HG)**. (I've had it and still can't pronounce it.) For those who still don't know what it is, it is extreme, debilitating sickness. Severe and prolonged nausea and vomiting, which can lead to dehydration and admission to hospital. It can last right up until the baby is born. So for those that say pregnancy is not an illness, for some it can be.

My sickness always started at week six of my pregnancies, and for my second it was like I woke up one day and couldn't stop throwing up from the moment I opened my eyes. At first I thought that maybe I had food poisoning, but two weeks in, I realized that it was something much more than food poisoning or the usual morning sickness.

I couldn't leave my bed. At one point, for reasons unknown to me, I ended up on the floor in our bedroom, wrapped in my duvet, with a sick bucket, throwing up constantly throughout the day. It got so bad that at one stage I hadn't made it down the stairs of the house or into a shower for two straight weeks, only managing to get up to use the toilet to pee and even that wasn't happening very often. Because I couldn't control my sickness, and I had no time or energy to make it to the toilet to be sick, a bucket was the only option. On a particularly bad day, Wayne called my obstetrician, who confirmed it was HG. He wanted me to come into hospital for a drip and observation, but there was absolutely no way that I was willing to move from my position on the floor, let alone get inside a moving vehicle. He agreed to let me stay at home, but made us promise that I had to come in if I felt I was losing consciousness from dehydration. In the meantime, he would send over some anti-sickness medication for me to try. But it was impossible to keep water down, let alone pills, and even moving my eyes made me throw up. I had never experienced anything like it in my life. It was a devastating experience as I already had Parker, my firstborn, my gorgeous little toddler, who I was already terrified would be too much affected by my pregnancy and a new baby in the house, and he was now not getting the mother he deserved. I couldn't leave my room, let alone get up and look after him. Even the smell of him made me sick. My mouth was constantly watering and the retching was starting to really hurt my throat and stomach.

I felt so alone and confused. Why was this happening to me? How was I going to make it through nine months of this? When would I be able to spend time with my child again? I didn't know when it would stop and this unknown made it even more overwhelming and horrifying. I remember just crying and crying, wondering if it was all worth it and then feeling awful for even thinking that way.

Anyone who's actually had morning sickness will know that it can occur at any time of the day – and sometimes all day and all night.

Of course I wanted this baby, but at what cost? I didn't want the child I already had to feel abandoned or unwanted. I was unable to do the work I had previously agreed to. And I was so very tired, and tiredness makes it a lot worse. And, mentally, I was starting to really struggle. I was letting so many people down. Work colleagues, my son, my husband and, again, myself.

My body just wouldn't let me enjoy a pregnancy. It felt as though my body didn't want me to become a mother. I lost half a stone and, after gaining four with the last pregnancy, I believed I'd brought this on myself, after being so scared to get 'fat' again like last time.

But, compared to some, I was lucky. The first type of anti-sickness medication I was given helped. For most women, it's a case of trial and error. The first medication may not work and they have to try out lots of different ones or a concoction of a few to alleviate the symptom. When the tablets started to work, I was finally able to walk downstairs, to the sofa. I still had my bucket permanently by my side and I was still being sick, but it was more manageable.

There were many more weeks like this. Eventually I was able to leave the house, but would always come home and be sick. It became the new normal.

Why was this happening to me? How was I going to make it through nine months of this?

There's just not enough known about this condition and not enough sympathy for those who struggle as it still falls under the umbrella term 'morning sickness'. And the truth is it's truly debilitating and some mothers have to spend a lot of time in and out of hospital. Mentally, it isn't a good place for any mother. The questioning of whether it's worth it and the guilt that comes with that. The guilt of what it will be doing to your unborn child and not being able to be the mum to the child you already have, or the wife and work colleague you should be. The sadness that you haven't enjoyed your pregnancy like you hoped to, or like other mothers seem to do. And then the fear that it will happen again if you ever want another baby.

Many women who suffer with the condition develop a form of PTSD, which doesn't surprise me, as it is a hugely conflicting and terrifying experience. Whenever a third child crosses my mind, it always comes with the fear of having two children I need to take care of and knowing that with HG, once you've had it, you're much more likely to get it again, so how would I be the mother my boys need me to be?

If you're currently suffering or have suffered, take the meds you're offered, go to hospital for that drip, don't feel guilty for any of it and I promise it absolutely IS worth it and you will get through it.

And for anyone who hasn't had it, *it is* an illness and *it isn't* morning sickness.

Trust me.

YOU'RE PUBLIC PROPERTY

From the moment you tell people you're pregnant, you begin to get their 'advice'. Mostly unsolicited.

I'm always conflicted between telling mothers-to-be how it really was for me and letting people find things out on their own, because all our experiences are completely individual. Something that one of us struggled with, the other might not.

Hearing someone's horrendous and complicated pregnancy or birth story is in some ways helpful, as it can prepare you for the worst and gives you insight into the fact that not everything is a perfect bed of roses. But on the flip side, you are also scaremongering and giving people something to worry about, when they're possibly already anxious or maybe just looking forward to finding out for themselves.

Whenever I met other expectant women or mums, they would gush about how much they loved their pregnancies and at first I would go along with it, but in the end I would say:

Yes, it's lovely, but I can't wait for the baby to be here.

I've felt so ill.

I'm not glowing.

It's not been what I expected and I've not really enjoyed it.

Then their stories would change and shift slightly. It was as though I was giving them permission to be honest and to be able to say how they really felt, instead of how they were expected to feel. It should be OK not to have the perfect pregnancy you imagined.

We need to accept feeling uncomfortable is part of life and we can't avoid it, and self-doubt and insecurity are normal. Vulnerability is normal and, who knows, if we behave in a paradoxical way, that is to say with more courage and letting go, we might achieve extraordinary things.

We need to remember:

- Embracing failure or perceived failure allows us to deal with life

- All stories of success involve failure in the journey

- We learn from failure

- Be wrong in a decision rather than freezing and avoiding.

Expectant mothers are pressured into living up to other people's expectations. Why is there such an obsession with how people's babies are delivered and why do we feel that our opinion is so important? Surely it makes no difference as long as the baby and mum are happy and healthy?

Expectant mothers are pressured into living up to other people's expectations.

I feel the media has a big role to play in this, since the whole 'too posh to push' era began. I'm not sure when huge abdominal surgery became seen as an easy way out: who decided it was? It feels to me a lot like disempowering mothers and making them feel even worse about their decisions – to what end, though? Birth is unpredictable and mostly out of anyone's control. If we survive and so does the baby, and we feel safe, as does our baby, where is the crime? Why are we made to feel guilty for having the painkillers? Not having the painkillers? Having the C-section? Having a water birth?

No matter what we do to deliver the baby safely, the world has an opinion.

No wonder women feel guilty about having a C-section, whether it's planned or an emergency. After having two elective C-sections, I've witnessed the judgement first-hand. The facial expression says more than the words. We don't always know people's reasons behind their decisions.

Aren't all births natural in their own way anyway?

I remember a male friend of mine asking what birth plan I had made. At this point, I hadn't decided. For some reason, he felt that he had a valid opinion and a say in the matter, and thought that all women should have a 'natural birth', as women had been doing it for thousands of years, all over the world. And of course he was right, they have. But the greatest killer of women up until the 20th century was childbirth! How lucky are we to live in a time and place where we have options? To be offered the choice. To choose painkillers if we need them. To have at-home births if we want them. To have an elected C-section if we think it would work best for us.

There are still so many women around the world who can't make these decisions and still have a high mortality rate during childbirth. Isn't the fact we can choose a privilege? A privilege that we should use and not waste?

I went in with an open mind to decide on my plan of action. I asked my obstetrician for the pros and cons of both. He gave me possible outcomes on how either birth could go, and we made the decision between us. My GP had told me to avoid an emergency C-section, and this advice had got stuck in my anxious brain. The knowledge of what would happen during an elected C-section made me feel a lot calmer about the whole thing. And that was important for me and my babies. What it definitely wasn't was a quick decision, a 'too posh to push' moment because I really couldn't be *bothered* with the whole 'giving birth' thing.

The recovery for both types of births can be long and hard, with their own physical and mental battles. I've had friends who had 'natural births' who felt they hadn't been warned of the recovery time or complications. Some who have had much longer recovery times than me. And having a C-section often leaves you unable to move or even pick up your baby for days. It is not an easy option. But it is an option.

Childbirth, regardless of what happens to you, has a cost. Just feel proud of having done it and that you arrived at a place where you and your baby are safe.

YOUR EXPECTATION OF WHAT KIND OF MOTHER YOU WILL BE

I had decided pretty early on in my life that I wanted to be a young parent. I had this fear of having success but having no one to share it with. I always knew that my kind of career was going to be short-lived and I didn't want mine to end abruptly without a family. Fortunately, this part of my plan went to *plan* when I met my husband as he felt the same way and from the start we shared a similar vision of the future we wanted to build together.

In truth, I hadn't ever given much thought to the fact that once you became a parent, your child is always going to be a part of your life. Not in the physical sense. From now on, whatever happens in your life, your children are always going to be such an intrinsic part of it that they will eventually redefine who you are in every way.

Because here's the thing: I knew adults who had children

who still worked,

who went abroad,

who went out with their friends,

who had their own lives,

who pursued their goals,

who were independent,

and so I presumed it was straightforward. Everything about our plan felt logical.

Have a child. Become a mum.
It will slot into your life!

Of course, some things would have to change, but mostly, everything would carry on as usual. I would remain the same.

And then I realized how wrong I was.

Everything changes.

Let me say that again.

EVERYTHING CHANGES.

Mostly in a good way, but it definitely changes.

Your life becomes unrecognizable.

YOU become unrecognizable.
Your mental health becomes unrecognizable.
Your emotions become unrecognizable.

And no one prepares you for this. It is as though it is 'the motherhood secret' that is all knowing looks and warm smiles and 'I knows', but no one **actually** tells you what to expect after you are expecting.

No one says, 'If you do this, it will be the greatest thing you ever do, but there is a lot that will never be the same again and it will be harder to find and carve out space for yourself in your own mind and those of other people too.'

No one asked me:

Why do you want to have a baby?

Do you have the time to meet the demanding needs of a child, like feeding, teaching them everything they know and keeping them entertained 24/7?

Do you have any other children?

If so, what age are they and how will they cope with this new addition to the family?

Are you committed to the cleaning and health maintenance of the child?

What is your attitude towards discipline and teaching manners?

How often is someone at home?

How committed are you to maintaining your current relationship?

Are you aware of the costs involved in having a child?

It really wasn't until a very good friend of mine had a baby that I realized how much pressure we put on ourselves, for our minds, lives and bodies to snap back to how they once were. I could sense, even though she was telling me that she was coping and appeared to be doing well, that deep down she was struggling and felt like an impostor.

She knew 'the rules' that she should keep this struggle locked up inside her, otherwise she was failing at being the mum, the woman and the courageous heroine she had been told she had to be. This invisible pressure that once you have become a mother everything needs to snap back into the neat frame and contours they once held. Rather than accepting and embracing the changes we have gone through, we are forced to disregard them in order to return ourselves to our former selves. Everything about our outer and inner appearance needs to return to how we were, regardless of the fact that everything about us – physically, mentally and emotionally – has radically changed.

So instead I told her to stop worrying about going back to the woman she was before, because that woman is no longer who she is; life is an endless procession of identities we inhabit and going back to a previous one is regressive. We need not to mourn our loss of our former self and instead embrace a new you. I said to her:

'You are not who you were before, you've carried and given birth to a human being and your life will never be the same again. This is a big adjustment, which relatively speaking has happened very suddenly to your life and, of course, it has completely changed you. It is one of the hardest and greatest things you will ever do. It will be sacrifice and fulfilment. Terror and euphoria. Deprivation and reward.'

My friend later told me that although she cried the whole way home in the car, from that moment on she felt so much better. The unnecessary pressure she had placed on herself had lifted and she understood that she couldn't be a mother yet remain the same person she was nine months before. It was unrealistic. Sure, you are still **you**, but you are a new, better version of you. Parts of you will remain, but a lot will change. She finally accepted and embraced this evolution and said goodbye to parts of herself which would never return. And it was a relief.

IMPOSTOR SYNDROME

Impostor syndrome has been widely written about and women in particular have led the way in taking the lid off the myths. It is not specific to women, but they are more inclined to experience it more intensely and be hampered by it.

Sheryl Sandberg, Facebook's Chief Operating Officer and one of the most successful women in business, wrote about it in her book *Lean In*: 'Every time I was called on in class, I was sure that I was about to embarrass myself, every time I took a test, I was sure that it had gone badly'. Sandberg believes that women struggle with impostor syndrome as they consistently underestimate themselves. Moreover, women will often attribute their successes to external factors such as working really hard, luck or help from others. When women fail, they attribute it internally to lack of ability, whereas when men fail, they attribute it externally – to not studying enough or not being interested in the subject.

70 per cent of women and 50 per cent of men report feeling impostor syndrome at some point in their lives.

Frankie's impostor syndrome tells her

I am not competent

I am not talented

I am an impostor

I was lucky

I am not a good mother

I don't enjoy spending time with the children

Wayne is better with the boys

In order for things to change, we all have to become more open and honest about how difficult motherhood can be. Here's my truth: in my seven-year journey of being a mum, I have had moments where I resented my new life, this 'new me' that I will never escape from being and society will always see me, and treat me, as. This doesn't mean that I have disliked or not loved my children wildly, but I have had times where I was unsure if the choice I had made of becoming a parent was the right one. Because I have always worried and questioned whether I am actually any good at it.

Can we please allow ourselves to say any negative thoughts or feelings about motherhood out loud, without having to say, 'I love my children, but' first? Struggling with, or finding parts you don't like about parenthood does not equate to you disliking your children. Nor should you ever be made to feel that way.

 Our thoughts and feelings are helpful
(but remember feelings aren't facts!)

I realized I had to find an equilibrium where I existed both as a mother and as me. I learned that this involved growing pains.

Some days will feel long, but the years are short. People tell you how fast it goes, and it really does!

I will battle with wanting to be a mum, but also still wanting to achieve my goals.

I will have days when I am grateful that my body produced my boys, but also resent that this experience has given me a body that I may never accept again.

I will be envious of my friends who can have a hangover and get a lie-in.

I will no longer have duvet days.

Accepting that no matter how old my boys are,
I will never relax.

Mum guilt is very real and very consistent.

My children won't necessarily fit into the mould that society or I expected them fit into, and neither will I, and that's OK.

My kids will always need a wee, even though I told them to go before we left.

Every time we go away as a family, it will feel like we are moving house. And just quickly popping out somewhere will never be possible again.

It's not all sunshine and rainbows, but it's not all thunder and showers either.

Newborns can be fascinating and cute, but they can also be pretty boring.

Sometimes you will feel like all you do is give to your baby and get nothing back, but the minute they start smiling at you, all is forgiven.

My relationship will need more attention, but will be better than it was before, if we take the time.

Anything after 5am will now be considered a lie-in.

I will learn to do everything with one hand.

Hot drinks and dinners will be a novelty.

I will eventually learn to trust my instincts, but equally always question them.

After the birth, I will continue to have contractions and it will hurt!

Sleep deprivation causes arguments and loss of patience, but you always manage to find the energy to do it all.

I will miss some of my life before kids, but that doesn't mean I regret my new one.

Yes, you will have to get rid of all of your shoes because your feet will grow a whole size during pregnancy and they will be replaced with much more sensible ones.

I will always feel guilty when I'm not with my kids, but instead of wasting that time not enjoying it,
I should embrace it.

Those times when I feel my kids are monsters and I question all my parenting skills: they really are just 'going through a phase'. **It will pass.**

YOUR LIFE BEFORE MOTHERHOOD

Twenty-four hours in my life, PM
(before I peed on a stick and found I was pregnant)

Disclaimer: Some things have been dramatized for the reader's enjoyment.

9am-ish. Slowly wake myself up and send Wayne to make me a cup of tea and bring it to me in bed.

9:45am Enjoy my hot cup of tea, while watching my favourite TV show.

10am Stay in bed and maybe even have an early morning quickie before we decide what to do for the day.

10:30am Finally get up, have a nice long shower or bath.

11am Do my hair and make-up, pick a nice outfit for the

day. (This was usually shortly before Wayne would decide on a random activity he wanted us to try, like archery, axe throwing or quad biking.)

11:30am Change out of a nice outfit, put something suitable on, walk out the door with nothing but my phone and purse.

12pm Do said activity, with varying degrees of success.

2pm Pick somewhere we both fancy, rock up without a booking, and get a table for two. Let lunch take as long as we want, sit next to each other, snuggled in and holding hands. Talking about our future, getting married and having cute babies. Decide on four children and that we would raise them on the GOOD STUFF, no chicken nuggets and chips, and not have iPads at the dinner table.

4pm Decide to see a new movie at the cinema that night. Book it online, see a movie rated eighteen.

7:30pm Grab a takeaway on the way home.

8pm Chill in front of the TV, eating our dinner, maybe even have a little cuddle, no interruptions and a few glasses of wine.

10:30pm Finally, go to bed when we can be bothered to walk upstairs, watch a bit more TV in bed, maybe even have sex and fall asleep naked.

My typical 24 hours having had children
AKA in the thick of it

5–7am Wake up whenever one of the boys, lying starfished in between Wayne and me, decides they don't want to sleep any more. (Hours before I've been able to get them up throughout the whole week, when I actually needed them up for school.)

6am Make as much noise as I possibly can, to see if I can get Wayne to get up instead of me, which he often 'can't hear'.

6:02am Try to convince the boys once more that they want a Mummy cuddle and to go back to sleep. *They don't.*

6:03am Slowly slide out of my bed like a sloth, with one eye open, already thinking of all the things I need to do that day, but can't be bothered to.

6:05am Go for a wee, with both boys watching, waiting impatiently for me to finish up and come downstairs.

6:06am Pick up a very wet, heavy nappy that's been taken off and thrown on the floor.

6:07am Put on yesterday's novelty PJs and walk down the stairs, already telling the boys, 'No, you can't have chocolate for breakfast, or watch YouTube'.

6:37am Continue the debate for at least another 30 minutes, before caving and giving them chocolate for breakfast.

6:38am Remind them to put their nappies in the bin.

6:39am Explain to them that they can't possibly be bored already, as we only just got up.

6:40am Make myself a cup of tea and take a sip before realizing I haven't put a teabag in the water.

6:45am Go upstairs and wake Wayne up with a passive-aggressive cup of coffee, while pretending that of course I'm not mad that he has had an extra half-hour in bed than me.

6:46am But I do remind him to put the bins out when he gets up because they stink.

6:47am Ask him what he thinks we should do

today as we have the kids at home with us all day again. Neither of us can think of anything new to do.

6:48am–12pm We take so long to decide how to keep the kids amused that it's too late to do anything.

12:01pm Make the boys yet another ham sandwich, with more chocolate after.

12:01pm onwards Spend the day telling them that, no, they can't have another snack.

12:08pm Watch Wayne and the boys play on the trampoline. I'm not invited to join in any more as I am 'the boring one' who's *rubbish at playing, Mummy.*

12:08–4:30pm Convince myself I'm an awful mother.

5pm Cook the boys fish fingers and chips for dinner and one piece of sweetcorn each, all while worrying they don't get enough healthy stuff.

5–6pm Battle to get them to eat said piece of sweetcorn.

6:15pm Fight to get them in the bath and clean their teeth.

6:30pm Give up trying to get them to sleep in their own beds and let them watch TV in ours.

6:32pm Come downstairs, Wayne asks what's for dinner. I say, 'Nothing unless you cook it or go and buy it, I'm too tired.'

6:35pm Decide on tea and biscuits and maybe a pint of G&T.

6:37pm As soon as my bum hits the sofa, one of the boys wanders downstairs and wants water and a snack delivered to him upstairs.

6:45pm Come back down, sit next to Wayne, start our latest episode of a new series we're sort of watching but can't remember any of the plot because we look at our phones throughout.

7pm I start to fall asleep

7:30pm Wayne suggests I go to bed. Leave him to tidy the kitchen, lock up and turn the lights off.

7:34pm Pass out in the only available space left on the bed because the boys and the dog have fallen asleep lengthways!

NB to any future mothers, this 24-hour cycle is now my children are older. A newborn is a very different 24 hours. For one thing, there are no longer hours or minutes or indeed morning and night. It is merely a cycle of keeping them alive as they poop, eat, sick, sleep, repeat.

Scenes from my life with a newborn

Any time of day or night Wake up to the sound of a crying baby, don't even open my eyes, wait to see if Wayne hears it. He doesn't.

Seconds later Drag the baby over to me, glance at the curtains to see if I can see light outside, just so I know what time of day it is. Wrestle with the baby to get him to latch on. Try my absolute hardest not to fall back to sleep and risk smothering the baby. Burp him, change his nappy, put him back down. Take Moses basket into the bathroom so I can wee and shower while seeing and hearing him. Doing everything as quickly as possible before he wakes up. Noticing that the floor is literally full of my hair that keeps falling out since I had the baby. Wondering if it's normal to lose this much hair?

Moments later While in the shower, I hear the baby crying, so rush out and throw on some huge over-the-belly-button knickers, as I have gained weight and had a C-section. Oh, and I'm still bleeding heavily: who knew that was even a thing?!

Seconds later Take him to his room and start changing him as he has done a poo. While I'm wiping his bum, he continues to go to the loo, then I realize my boobs are leaking milk.

Milliseconds later Try to stick cotton pads onto my nipples in the hope that they will stick. Realize this isn't working. Scream for some help, Wayne looks at me horrified, not really knowing how to help or what to do. Turn around to see the dog taking a poop on the carpet. Briefly think, *This seriously can't be what it's like for everyone else?*

Seconds later Deposit baby with Wayne. Run out of the room dressed only in my big knickers, and my sister's boyfriend (who I remember now has come to stay, with my sister, to help us) is standing stock still in the hallway. We look each other in the eye, both unable to say a word, both mentally scarred. Run away wondering, *Why did I think the cotton wool pads would stick to my nipples?* Make my way downstairs, hair still wet, clean PJs on, baby in Moses basket. Plop on the sofa, where I spend the rest of my day. Feeding, burping and changing nappies. Look at the clock and realize it's still only **10am.**

These are obviously big extremes, or are they?

YOUR LIFE NO LONGER BELONGS TO YOU

You take your baby home, close the front door and then the reality hits. This is it, for ever. It can be exhilarating and downright terrifying at the same time. Everything you may have learned in antenatal classes or NCT is often forgotten amid the fog that is mummy brain (and daddy brain too). I have seen the most powerful high-paid executives, and indeed even newly parented consultant paediatricians, develop (transient!) cognitive impairment overnight where they cannot manage the most basic of tasks, unable to string a sensible sentence together.

Your previous life's peace is shattered the first time you hear the piercing sound of the baby's high-pitched screaming. Most commonly, this will happen late at night. If you are breast feeding, then the onus is all on your shoulders, already buckling under the strain of your rapidly engorging breasts. The obvious problem, 'Are you hungry?' No, not interested. OK, must be the nappy then. Nope, all clean. 'What is it then?' you implore the little one to respond intelligently without any success. Next step, the Viennese waltz around the room, jiggling and rocking. No luck. OK, into the buggy for a walk. It's 2am by now, and it's winter and the latest storm, named Serenity, is in full force (the irony). 'Please stop crying,' you are now begging.

And this is just day one.

Finally, the baby yields to sleep, and you get into bed, sopping wet, from the tears as well as the deluge, and collapse into a deep stupor. Out of your coma you feel the tugging of your helpless partner, telling you the baby is screaming again (at first you may hear nothing, your senses are in deep shock). It's been just 30 minutes. You feel a failure already and utter a profanity and then feel even more guilt and hope this is not the first word that will eventually come out of your toddler's mouth.

A new baby is unconditionally dependent upon you and this can certainly be overwhelming. In the first weeks, you may well feel hyperalert and hypervigilant and insecure in your ability to manage the baby and manage yourself. This is particularly true of the breast-feeding mum. Even the little things you had always taken for granted become major military operations. Trying to have a poo (you, not the baby) can be hard (literally so, if you have been holding it in and not gone for a few days!). Your whole routine goes out the window, your independence has gone. It takes time to adapt to this new life. Perhaps one of the clearest manifestations of the loss of their previous life and independence is the sleep deprivation, one of the oldest forms of torture. But it is amazing how even the most discombobulated new parents that I see in my clinic in the first week of their baby's life can transform from their anxiety-ridden and cognitively challenged state into confident caregivers within weeks.

Some babies are easy, and even if feeding every three to four hours through the night will do so efficiently and quickly, an easy burp, change of nappy and back to sleep, and so the parents also can have good stretches of quality sleep. (It is often the most annoying ones in the NCT class who boast of this feat, their babies being the ones who will walk at six months and talk two languages fluently by nine months.) Meanwhile, on Planet Reality, babies will often not follow the rules of polite and compliant engagement. Indeed, the most common reason I see young infants is for crying and fussy feeding, which tend to be inextricably linked.

Parents are desperate for solutions, and while it is of course possible there is an underlying medical reason – such as acid reflux giving the baby heartburn, or an allergic reaction to the milk, either breast or formula – the vast majority do not have anything wrong with them. Colic is still not understood, over 400 years since it was first described. Babies definitely suffer from abdominal distension and a lot of gas, and this seems to coincide with episodes of screaming, particularly in the evening. They can writhe around and arch their backs, which is similar to the symptoms caused by reflux or milk allergy, so we always have a challenge working out the best strategy to help these babies. I prefer what we call watchful waiting (in other words, siting on my hands until the storm passes).

We readily advise mums to cut out all dairy (often with little or no evidence of likely causation) as it is a seemingly benign intervention. Yet it can add insult to injury – having suffered all the discomfort of nine months of heartburn and haemorrhoids, the pain and indignity of delivery, they must now sacrifice one of their pleasures in life – that morning cappuccino or macaroni cheese for dinner. For some, though, this sacrifice is worth it as the baby can be transformed (although that is not commonly the case).

No one told me about night sweats.

That was something I really could have done with a heads-up about.

The sensation of your hormones beginning to return to normal is almost as bad as your hormone levels getting higher when you first become pregnant. I have never been someone to sweat. I could dance and sing for an hour and a half, under the hot lights of a stage, and just have a slight glow. So this was not something I was expecting. I'd wake up in the night, soaking wet and unbearably hot. So even when I finally got my baby sleeping, I remained awake. As far as I'm aware, I've never had BO before, but I certainly did now! Weirdly, though, it was only in one armpit. Maybe that was a blessing? I remember embarrassingly bringing up the whole smelly sweat thing with my obstetrician and he said it was totally normal. I was relieved, but still so horrified and wondering how long it was going to last for. My body felt as though it didn't belong to me.

It seems like something so small and trivial, but at the time, it felt like yet another thing that was outside my control and happening to my body.

Bleeding after birth

Who knew that it would last so long? I had heard that you bleed a lot after having a baby. I remember the horror and disbelief in the size and thickness of the sanitary towels that were suggested! I packed the packet of maternity pads and normal sanitary towels in my hospital bag, as I couldn't fathom that I would possibly need these 'nappies' I was told I would.

After coming out of surgery you have a catheter and a huge sanitary towel, none of which I was aware of as I was still numb. Although, I'm not going to lie, the relief of a catheter was amazing after spending nine months peeing constantly – not to mention having to perfect my aim of peeing into the smallest pots ever known to man at every antenatal appointment and trying to avoid peeing on my hands! Why do they make those pots so small? It's hard enough to aim before you have a bump, let alone when you do and can no longer see your bits!

I didn't know I had the huge sanitary towel on until I had my first shower and the lovely nurse helping me up and into the shower whipped it out from between my legs with no warning. Bye bye, dignity. That first shower felt like a dream, unlike the first wee. Now, I can imagine, the first wee after a vaginal birth is a million times worse than after a C-section, but it's still not an enjoyable experience. It feels like it takes for ever to come out and when it does, it's like it lasts for ever! First off, you're not allowed to close the door and it has to be done in a bowl, so that it can be checked after. Mine was made even less enjoyable by my sister and my two friends watching the whole thing. It is not a group activity!

Anyway, the bleeding feels like it lasts for ever. Mine wasn't as heavy as some. I think with a section it's slightly less. However, it's like the longest period of your life. Which doesn't help with the whole feeling-back-to-yourself situation.

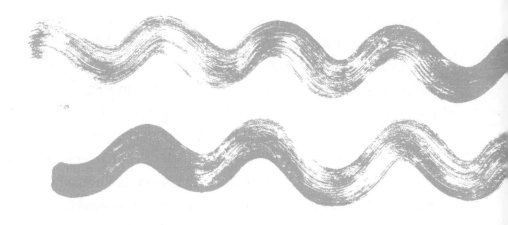

YOUR LACK OF CONTROL

A lot of my anxieties come down to lack of control. And I have never felt so out of control in my life as when I got pregnant and then became a parent.

I knew that for my mental health I would opt for a C-section as at least then I would have control over one aspect of the birthing experience. But the shame of a C-section is still real before anyone's even passed a comment.

That sense of embarrassment and shame has haunted me whenever I talk about the fact that both my babies were elected C-sections, as though I am not really part of the Mum Club because I didn't have a 'natural birth'. I used to get so bored of that conversation.

'How was
the birth?'

'I had a C-section'.

'Emergency?'

'No, elected'.

'Oh!'
Judgy face.

But I knew that it would help my spiralling anxiety and I was fortunate enough to be able to make that decision. The downside was that the C-section meant Parker wasn't able to remove all the mucus in his throat during birth (remember when I said every type of childbirth comes at a cost?), which led to him having to do so for a few days longer than a baby who is born vaginally. (Notice I didn't say 'naturally'. How are we still using that term?)

At the hospital, the nurses would offer to take Parker for small periods of time so that I could get some proper sleep. I never said yes, I wanted to keep him in my sight at all times. I would just lie there staring at him. I couldn't believe I had created this baby and I was fascinated by everything that he did. Until one afternoon, while he was sleeping on his back, he started choking. The fear shot through me like an unbearable pain. I started shouting for a nurse desperately and stabbing wildly at the alarm button. I couldn't get out of bed fast enough to grab him and I knew he was choking on the mucus. The whole ordeal was resolved pretty quickly, but I was left utterly terrified and shaken to the core. So, I finally gave up control, for the first time since becoming a mother, and asked them to watch him for a little while. I was convinced that he would be safer with them than with me. This was my first experience of doing everything I was told was best for my baby, yet still being all too close to danger. After that,

I can do my best to protect and look after my children, but at some point they will cry or get hurt.

I feared whenever he slept on his back, convinced that he would choke every time. But this experience also taught me a big lesson: I can do my best to protect and look after my children, but at some point they will cry or get hurt.

I had spent most of my life believing that it was down to me to keep everyone I loved happy and safe – huge task for one person, let alone a child. I had spent years in therapy before this, being told that I couldn't control and take care of everyone – talking about it over and over. But it took having kids for me to really grasp it. And although I still have this knee-jerk need to fix things and have a constant fear of people getting sick or injured, I fundamentally came to accept that it was impossible.

I can watch my children running and playing and tell them to slow down and watch where they're going, yet they can still fall over and scrape their knees.

I can do my best to teach them to be kind, considerate to humans and to simply play with someone else if someone is not nice to them. But they will cry at some point in their life. They are going to fall down and feel like they haven't got anyone to catch them and they will learn to pick themselves back up. And they will learn that loss is a part of growth.

This is how they learn and become the people they will become, but it doesn't mean it's easy to give them the space and freedom to grow.

YOUR EMOTIONS NO LONGER BELONG TO YOU

I was pretty calm after having my first baby. The hospital felt safe, we were well looked after and the baby and I were healthy. I couldn't have asked for more. There were moments of stress, but for me, to not feel anxious was a miracle. Once we left the hospital and went home, however, it was a whole other story.

 Nothing that you learned in your NCT classes, or books such *What to Expect...* prepares you for the first night at home.

Unless they've had a Caesarean, mothers are encouraged to spend less than one night in the hospital after giving birth (grandmothers say that they were able to spend a week there in the old days, but I am also told that in those days babies were left parked in their prams outside supermarkets . . . !)

The baby's Moses basket will probably not get used on the first night. Baby will probably sleep in the bed with you. If you think of cave men and women, I bet they didn't put their children to sleep in the cave next to the one they were in!

When the baby is inside you, there's a part of you that knows the safety of your baby is mainly out of your hands. The body just magically does most of it for you. There's a fluid to protect them and an umbilical cord to feed them. We can help even further with the foods we eat and the actions we take. But once the baby is out, it's all on you.

You now have to protect them from so much in the world and everyone in it, for the rest of their lives. I had such dark thoughts and worries.

I suddenly realized that this tiny human that I've only just met and known for a few days would be the absolute making of me and bring me pure joy, but that he also had the ability to completely destroy me. If anything was to ever happen to him, and he wasn't here any more, my life would be over. Even if he was to be hurt or sad, I knew I would feel that physically for the rest of my life.

Now, the fact that Parker cried the whole way home didn't help, it was as though we were cast off from the mainland, stranded out in the big wide ocean of parenthood all alone. We just had to figure out how to keep things afloat.

The love I had for this new little baby was overwhelming and terrifying. People tell you the love for your child is like no other, but until you've felt it, you can't explain it or imagine it. I had tried to compare it to my love for Wayne or my family. But it's incomparable. Almost too much to bear. Or think about too much. Every time the baby cried, which was often, I cried.

Before I had a baby, I was aware that when they cried it mainly meant they were tired, hungry, wanted cuddles and sometimes were uncomfortable. But now he was here, I took it personally. It was a sign I was failing and I truly believed he was deeply unhappy or scared. I was already rubbish at the one thing I had always wanted to do. It got to the point that only Wayne could calm him, as I would work myself up so much and just sob all over him. Wayne had a calmness about him and could take the crying for what it was. He had the bonus of not having hormones coursing through his body too though . . .

Trusting yourself

Something I found hard to get my head around was this notion that I would intuitively know what to do with a baby. That's what everyone tells you will happen to you. But I was so worried that I'd be that one mum for whom it didn't. I read all the baby books, downloaded all the apps, but still, how would I know?

The only experience I can liken this feeling to is your first kiss. When you're getting to that age when all your friends are doing it and you're thinking, *How the hell do they know what to do?* And when you ask them, they all just say, 'I dunno, you just do.' It's that. And guess what? Just like that first awkward, messy, fumbly, wet first kiss, eventually you figure it out. But you aren't brilliant at it straight away.

That's exactly what happens with your baby. You don't meet someone and automatically expect to know all their quirks, wants and needs. So why do we expect ourselves to know with a newborn? You learn as you go. Sometimes you get it wrong, but eventually you learn what works for you both.

With my firstborn, I bought all the stuff. Everything in Mothercare was in my house. I tried every formula, dummy, bottle, nappy. You name it, I tried it.

Whoever you are, you're always going to question yourself,

you're always going to have some sort of guilt as a parent,

you're always going
to wonder if what
you're feeling is
normal.

But the thing is,
we all want the
same outcome.

A happy,
healthy child.

OCD AND INTRUSIVE THOUGHTS

New mothers have a huge sense of responsibility, as they acutely feel a need to keep the newborn safe. Obsessive compulsive disorder can be seen in some new mothers. OCD is often fixated on people important to the person who is struggling. They don't want to cause any harm to the most helpless and precious little thing.

The added responsibility fuels obsessions, often around letting harm come to the baby. 'What if the baby's head suddenly goes under the water in the bathtub?' 'What if I accidentally roll over my baby when I am sleeping?' These thoughts are completely normal. However, parents can start to believe that if they have that abhorrent thought, then there must be some part of them that wants it to happen. They then avoid being with the baby, which makes matters worse.

The OCD mantra has to be 'a thought is just a thought, a thought is not an intention, a thought is not a behaviour'.

Recent research has shown that 15 per cent of new mothers report intrusive thoughts, and we need to help them to normalize these. Again, please speak to your GP or health visitor if you are worried.

Frightening, intrusive thoughts come to all of us. Most of us can dismiss them and move on. Others are horrified by the thoughts, increasing their frequency and interfering with our functioning.

The occurrence of OCD thoughts is universal and historical. The best book I have read and recommend to all of my clients with obsessional thoughts is *The Imp of the Mind* by Lee Baer.

YOUR LIFE CHANGES

The first step into motherhood and I really struggled to find my feet. I thought that being a stay-at-home mum would be enough for me. I had worked and been successful from the age of 12 and I felt that I would now be happy to devote my life to being a wife and a mum.

Parker and I went to all the baby classes and activity groups we could fit into our days and I devoted myself to bringing him up. I spent all the hours in both of our days keeping him entertained and trying to make him happy and would do everything and anything I could for him. But after a while, I started to long for more.

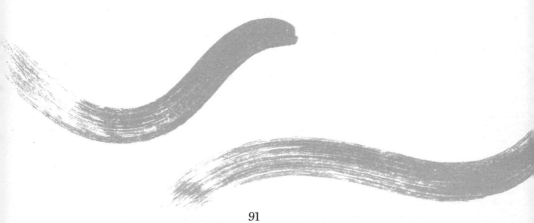

I wasn't used to this calm, sedate life of being at home alone with a child who didn't respond to me. I didn't know who I was without a schedule and being told what to do from day to day. What I had achieved in the years before I became a mum had sculpted me and I was used to ambitiously striving for the next thing which could prove my worth. And so my mind and my depression began to tell me that I was now a failure. It wouldn't allow me to appreciate and be proud of all I had achieved and was still achieving with my son and being his mother. Which conversely also brought with it an onslaught of guilt.

Why wasn't my gorgeous boy enough?
Did I not love him enough?
Why was this enough for other mums but not for me?
Was I a bad parent?

But I had been taught that being successful at life meant being busy 24/7, 365 days of the year and with it came acclaim, recognizability and earning my own money. My new role as a mother didn't lean into any of my perceptions of success and I soon found myself feeling that I had failed once again.

Before this revelation, I had been envious of stay-at-home mums without ever perceiving the underlying rivalry between them and working mums. To me, going to work was almost like a day off. A day to be myself, to get dressed up, put on some make-up and to have an adult conversation and be treated like an adult, not a mother. I longed to be a parent who was more than happy to stay home all day and to devote her life to her child. But that would have involved splintering off too much of who I was and what made me happy.

YOUR 'ROLES'

As I had C-sections with both my boys, Wayne did the first few nappies. He didn't have any other choice than to get stuck in straight away. As time went on, we fell into our roles and they have remained pretty cemented ever since. And truthfully, I don't think I've had a deep night's sleep since Parker was born.

It's like you literally sleep with one eye open. Ready and waiting for someone to need you at any given moment. I'm still the same now. It drives my husband mad, as I wake up asking 'Where are you going? What are you doing? You OK?'

There have been countless nights where I have been sitting up with one of the boys who is scared, tired, ill or wanting love and I look over at Wayne still fast asleep and I wonder, is this a skill or a choice?! But ultimately I think it is about working out what you can do. What doesn't work for you and where you need support.

What is your limit?

When does it overwhelm you?

What can help?

What doesn't help?

All these things are part of the negotiation of parenting and looking after yourself at the same time. How much you can do without losing yourself in the process.

how . . .

HOW DO I BREASTFEED?

We all know 'breast is best', we've had it drummed into our heads enough. Even the term 'fed is best' annoys me. There shouldn't really be a need for all these slogans to make everyone feel better. If I had my way, it would be *'whatever works for you and your baby is best'* (not so catchy, I know).

But that's all that matters. I went into breastfeeding with quite a laid-back attitude. My husband was very supportive, and happy for me to do whatever felt right for me, so I felt I would try to do it and hope it worked but not drive myself mad if it didn't. The pressure was off. If the father of my child wasn't fussed either, then whose business was it other than ours?

I decided I would definitely do the first colostrum feed and then give the rest of it a go and see how I felt. Colostrum is described as 'liquid gold'. It's loaded with immune, growth and tissue-repair factors, and helps in the development of immunity in newborns. So kind of a big deal. Funnily enough and much to my surprise, the first time Parker latched on in recovery, it felt amazing. My firstborn was here and I could provide him with everything he needed. It made me feel close to him and that first time was bliss.

But after that, I had a rude awakening. All of a sudden, my boobs were no longer mine. A nurse came in, what felt like every five minutes, with a syringe to catch the colostrum from my nipples. She would massage my breast and squeeze them until something dropped out. It felt like a lot of work and manhandling for a rice-sized bit of liquid. She would then hold the syringe and suck it up. I couldn't believe it – my body had always been my own domain and now it was suddenly public property and not for my private use but for the wellbeing of my child!

My nipples felt so sore and raw. My milk didn't come in for a few days, due to the C-section, and Parker never cried or woke up for milk while we were in hospital. When my milk did come in, it was like I was gearing up to feed the five thousand. And I fortunately had incredible maternity nurses in the hospital who made it their mission to help me to get to grips with

breastfeeding as much as possible before I left to go home. But as soon as we left, he cried the whole way home and didn't stop till what felt like he was five.

Feeding him was a constant battle. He struggled to latch on properly and the pain of my raw, scrabbled nipples was sometimes unbearable, but I persisted. I think mainly out of guilt that this was what I was supposed to do. After about a month of breastfeeding, I started to feel fed up with the isolation of it all. We weren't out and about at all, but even when friends or family visited, I didn't feel comfortable whipping a boob out. Mainly because I couldn't do it the way I saw other women doing it. Slightly lifting up my top or placing a muslin over my shoulder and the baby instantly knowing what to do. I had to pretty much grab my breast, rub it in Parker's face and shove it in his mouth, over and over again until he finally figured out if he wanted it or not and what to do with it. So I'd take myself to a room on my own and he'd feed for what felt like hours. I felt this huge pressure of being the only person that was solely responsible for his nutrition. It started to scare me and felt like too much responsibility. The final straw came during one of Wayne's football games. It was the first time I had taken Parker out and he just wouldn't feed. He was crying, I was crying and I decided there and then, enough was

I couldn't believe it – my body had always been my own domain and now it was suddenly public property.

enough. I had brought a bottle and some formula with me as back-up and decided to give it a go. Filled with guilt and dread, I put it in Parker's screaming mouth. He guzzled the whole bottle and was happy as Larry. The pressure fell from my shoulders instantly. If he was happy, I was happy, and he was fed. I pumped the whole way home and I laughed at how much life had changed. And how much I was yet to learn.

Only later I was told that the reason Parker had not latched on was because my breasts were too engorged with milk, so the skin and nipple were too tight, so technically he had nothing to latch on to.

I was so scared of then getting mastitis that I constantly massaged my breasts to avoid the milk ducts from getting blocked and walked around with big cabbage leaves in my bra to encourage them to dry out. Which made me feel even further removed from the person I was. As you can imagine!

It was then that Parker really stepped up the crying. He seemed like he was constantly in pain. Arching his back, screaming and screaming. Something clearly wasn't right and the guilt crept back in quickly. *Maybe if I had just persisted with the breastfeeding, he wouldn't be in this mess?* He also only went to sleep if he was held upright, so sleep was definitely off the menu for us.

Sleep deprivation is a gift that comes home with your baby. However, just like breathing, sleep is not a voluntary activity. Sleep is necessary and comes naturally: women can fall asleep while feeding, while sitting at the table and so on. When we are sleep-deprived, nature tries to make the most of the little sleep that we do get.

All good midwives and health visitors will tell you that you should sleep when the baby is asleep. Ever tried that? Instead, that's when parents have a chance to shower, put the washing machine on or sterilize bottles. In cultures where large extended families are the norm, things are different, because no baby would be left alone with just the newbie parents! This may mean you get more sleep, but you will also be bombarded with instructions on everything under the sun by your relatives.

Frankie always struggled with sleep and after Parker was born, it only got worse. She also uses sleep as a form of hibernation. It is a passive strategy, but effective, because she can give herself a break and stay under the covers.

Sleep is often the first thing that goes when our mood is low or our anxiety is high. It is also often the last thing to return to normal

Every day, we build up sleep debt. If we wake up at 7am and it is now 10am, we are now in three hours of sleep deprivation (the debt). As the day goes on, we are more and more in debt. We pay this debt back when our circadian clock tells us to sleep in the evening. To help re-set our internal clock, it is essential to get some exposure to daylight in the mornings.

Washing was no longer an essential part of my day either. It took me a really long time to be able to feel comfortable with the baby being out of my sight. Showers were short, hair and body half washed, no time to dry, let alone brush, my hair. I was starting to transition into the half-mother, half-survival mode of the first few years.

As we tried to get to the bottom of Parker's constant screaming, I tried every formula out there to see if this was the problem. Doctors prescribed him ranitidine and Gaviscon for colic and reflux, but nothing seemed to help. Eventually I met Ed, a paediatrician, who suggested that Parker might have an intolerance to the protein in cow's milk. Something I had never heard of before and no one else had ever suggested. He prescribed us a special formula and told us it would take a few weeks for his body to adjust. The formula smelt like cheese and I remember sobbing as I fed it to him. Convinced if it smelled that awful, then it must be bad for him. However, Parker didn't seem to notice and drank the whole bottle.

A big part of all the confusion and conflicting advice is that times change. The rules change from year to year. Which way baby should sleep. Where they should sleep. How to prepare a bottle. I remember the first night my Mum was going to do the night feeds, so I could get some sleep, I went into her bedroom to check she had everything she needed. She had all the babies' bottles made up by the side of her bed.

I was like, 'Mum! You can't do that, you have to prepare each bottle at the time of the feed.' 'Really, why? It's all boiling water and it's how I used to do it for you girls.' 'It's all changed now, Mum, something to do with bacteria in the formula.'

She couldn't get her head around it, as neither of us had ever got sick from it. I realized then that that's where the issues come from. She was right, we were fine, but we know more now than we did then. And although I'm sure Parker would have been fine, again, if he wasn't, I would have only blamed myself and for me that's what it always comes down to. My gut. And as parents, I think that's what we should always stick with and listen to, no matter what anyone else says, as at the end of the day, it's on no one else but you. Scary, but empowering! Another lesson in learning how to be a mother for your child's needs rather than thinking that one size fits all.

We strongly advocate breastfeeding as there are clear advantages to the baby, but there are so many caveats to this. Mothers are placed under a great deal of health-professional and societal pressure to breastfeed. While most can breastfeed easily, and the baby latches well, for others it is a miserable journey, which ends when their nipples wave the white flag, beaten into submission by the incessant and unrelenting assaults on them. Even without teeth, a baby can destroy the hardiest nipple, reduced to a cracked, bleeding vestige of its former self.

There is such guilt associated with stopping breastfeeding (and for those who cannot start due to medications they are taking or who simply choose not to). As paediatricians, we try to support mums in their decisions and have to walk the fine line between knowing breast milk does confer advantages, but also that a mother who is struggling, not getting sleep and in pain is better off switching to formula milk than risking her mental health and her ability to otherwise care for the baby.

With breastfeeding, partners often feel excluded by not
being involved, and further distanced from the mums,
exacerbating their frustrations by the self-evident fact
that it is hard to find the time and the inclination for sex
in between breastfeeds, burping, passing gas (mum and
baby, given the inevitable consequences of eating on
the run) and nappy changes. Further, in the early days,
if the mum has had a Caesarean section or a vaginal
delivery that resulted in tears and sutures, this is yet
more disincentive for intimacy. This is important, and the
partner can feel isolated and dissociated.

HOW TO FEEL THE FEAR AND LET THEM DO IT ANYWAY

When our instincts tell us to protect, comfort and prevent our children from harm or sadness, how do we manage and process that our fears of this happening may actually hinder their individual progress or understanding of the world?

One of the big questions as a parent of a young baby is whether or not to let them cry out. Do you go in and console them, or do you practise controlled crying? Both my children cried a lot, but particularly my first, and if there is a crying method I have not Googled and tried I would be amazed.

I found all methods extremely difficult. Because a crying baby is difficult. And nothing can prepare you for how it makes you feel, hearing your baby cry and cry and cry.

In my mind as a mother, when one of my babies cried in the night, they were scared and needed me. I never wanted them to feel that they were alone. To me, that was unthinkable. So I would try to comfort them whenever they were upset and let them know that I was there, and always would be, to reassure them and mop them up. They never had to fear being left alone. I would be endlessly cuddling, rocking, shhhing, comforting them and then trying to transfer them back to the cot without waking them, and often waking them and having to start the whole process back over.

Once they were back in the cot, I would then have to begin the terrifying creep to the door, hoping that I wouldn't be noticed, and then attempt to slowly close the door. As they got older, I would often be found asleep in the cot with them. Which progressed to me lying on the floor next to the cot, with a hand through one of the gaps, holding them. But this level of attentiveness was draining and my nerves were starting to prickle with anxiety from my hypervigilant state. I felt that in order to keep going I needed to set some boundaries in place, as much for the baby as for me. We both were too reliant on each other.

And so, when Parker was about one and a half, and was probably aware of what he was doing and had figured out my response to his tears would always be undivided attention, to a certain extent he had begun to 'try his luck'. We Googled the 'crying out method' and thought that we should try it out for his sake as well as both of ours. The method is also called 'the extinction method', but if that doesn't scare you and put your mother's anxiety into overdrive I don't know what will! The concept is essentially a sleep-training technique and you are supposed to put your baby in their crib fully awake and the idea is that you just allow them to fuss, scream, wail and cry until the method tells you they will fall asleep from tiredness and without you there to comfort them, which means you won't feed to sleep, rock to sleep or basically support or aid your baby's natural drift off to sleep.

But the problem was, as soon as one of us entered or left the room, it only made his crying worse. That boy had the ability to cry for hours relentlessly and without tiring! So the method was entirely hopeless for us. It only exacerbated the problem.

The next night we tried another method which was more DIY: when I heard him cry I put headphones on and made sure the baby monitor was on silent. A friend of mine had told me to listen to music, so that I wouldn't get agitated and upset by the sound of my baby crying, but that I should still sit and watch the baby monitor. We were trying to find a way for me to safely let him cry without getting distressed myself and caving. So I popped in my headphones and watched and waited. And it worked! He didn't cry for half as long as he normally did if I was trying to settle him and he finally soothed himself, with one of the 20 million dummies I used to line his bed with, so that he could always find one. I was amazed and relieved that it had worked.

Later that night, I went in to check on him and the minute I opened the door, a terrible smell hit me. He had thrown up all over his cot and had then gone to sleep in it. This wasn't anything new, as he would often make himself sick because he was crying so hard, but this time, as I wasn't in and out of his room, I hadn't seen or heard it.

The guilt I felt was unbelievable. I hugged him so tightly and swore I'd never leave him to cry again. And that I would always be there for him and I wouldn't try any of these methods again, I would just be there when he needed me. (Fast forward to this day, the kid still always ends up in our bed.)

However, my secondborn was the typical second child. He slept perfectly, mainly because he didn't have a choice. We weren't going to be running to him if he didn't, because we were still spending so much time trying to settle his older brother. That is, until he was old enough to realize that his big brother was getting into Mummy and Daddy's bed and he wanted in on the action too.

⬤ Sleep requirments by age, as recommended by The National Sleep Foundation:

Newborn (0–3 months): 14–17 hours
Infant (4–11 months): 12–15 hours
Toddler (1–2): 11–14 hours
Preschooler: 10–13 hours

☀ The numbers listed above are the recommended sleep requirements for children. However, for many, this is just a dream (the irony). Parents ask me all the time about the amount of sleep their baby or child should get, mainly because they are worried that it seems a lot less than their peers. Some children simply need less (and some spend most of their waking moments asleep, if that's not a contradiction!). Occasionally medical issues can disrupt sleep, for example enlarged adenoids causing snoring and sleep apnoea, waking the child up, but in the vast majority of cases there is nothing wrong. I never advise keeping tabs on total duration of sleep; they will have as much as they need.

An extension of never wanting to see my children crying is my fear of taking them for their immunizations. As someone with a fear of needles, having to take my precious cargo, who I have coddled and protected from any harm, to be prodded and pricked made me feel anxious. Especially knowing that the injections were going to make them feel pretty unwell and that there was a calculated, albeit negligible, risk involved that I was exposing them to. While I never once considered not getting them immunized, my maternal instinct screamed and railed about the safety of my children and the risk that I was exposing them to. But equally, I knew and accepted that if they ever became ill from a terrible disease I could have immunized them against, I would not be able to live with myself and the guilt. It was when my own anxiety overlapped into their safety that I found early decisions hardest. It was the realization that my own demons had to be put aside in order to do the best I could as a mother. It wasn't easy. It isn't easy.

The guilt I felt was unbelievable. I hugged him so tightly and swore I'd never leave him to cry again.

But I did come up with a very clever way to get around this at the appointments. Both Mummy and Daddy would go to the appointment together, but we had two very different roles to play. It was essentially a game of good cop, bad cop. Daddy would be bad cop; so he would have to take hold of the baby while the jab happened, then I played good cop, and would take them away from the bad man (the doctor) and cuddle and console them, to make it all better. This enabled me to still comfort them and not be directly involved in the aspect that made my anxiety spiral.

However, after a few years of synchronized tag teaming, I had to go it alone. I had been advised (not by Dr Ed, the paediatrician who has contributed to this book) to give Parker the chickenpox vaccine, which is not part of the routine childhood vaccination schedule. At the time, we had a nanny, something we thought we needed but in hindsight probably didn't, but it helped me to feel that if I needed the support it was there. Just in case. The nanny came to the appointment with me, to be the bad cop.

A judgemental doctor asked,
'Is this your nanny?'

'Yes.'

'Oh. Why have you brought her with you?'

'Because I'm scared of needles.'

'So you work full time then?'

'Yes, normally, but not right now.'

'Oh, so why do you need a nanny then?'

'Erm . . .'

In that moment, I felt incredibly judged about my life choices and decisions as a parent. It was humiliating and I felt unfit, and this compounded my own battles with never feeling good enough. A failure. A let down.

Later that night, Parker didn't seem very well, so I called Dr Ed to check that his symptoms were normal after having had the vaccine. Ed said Parker was absolutely fine, but also that he should not have been given the vaccine until he was at least one year old. I had been badly advised. The guilt and fear I had felt throughout the day spiralled, and spiralled badly. And it resulted in a complete meltdown. My paranoia kicked into overdrive too and I became convinced I had killed my child, before he'd even really got the chance to live. Although he was fine and it just meant that the vaccine might not work and was therefore a complete waste of time. But it was at moments like this when my own mental health and battles that I struggled with crept into my sense of who I was as a mother.

I was a failure.

A waste of space.

Bound to let my kids down.

The truth is that the surgery should have known and checked his birth date and booked us in at a date that would have worked. But I didn't see this, I only saw what a failure I *was*.

 Frankie internalizes failure. She needs people to believe in her and to be her cheerleaders.

This is the trope of the perfectionist – you have to get everything right. Frankie sets high standards for herself. Unfortunately, when she fails to meet some of them, she internalizes the failure and experiences worry and self-doubt. Perfectionists find it difficult to delegate, because they see this as a failure. Frankie also finds it difficult to celebrate success, and always thinks about how she could have done things better.

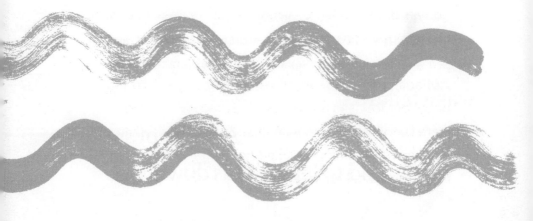

CRYING

 Just as the first wave of fear begins to dissipate, a sleep and feeding routing is established and you think you've cracked it, the baby decides things are getting far too easy for you and they need to step it up a gear. So begins the sleep regression and crying. Once more they have you guessing: are they in pain, hungry, or are they just trying to wind you up? This is a really difficult phase.

Crying is the most powerful tool in your baby's box, and in most situations they know you will come. And you do. Over and over. Some people in your NCT group may tell you not to let the baby cry, others will tell you the opposite.(Except for our annoying friend whose baby never cries, of course. But don't worry about them. One day karma will get them.) It is so confusing. There is no simple answer and I tend never to direct parents on how they should react as each family is different, every baby is different. What is indisputable is the stress that a crying baby can cause.

As health professionals, if we are asked to assess the baby, our job is to ensure as far as practicable that there is nothing wrong with them. A simple indication is how the baby reacts if picked up: an immediate return to a settled, smiling baby tells us all we need to know.

On the other hand, if the baby remains inconsolable it is likely they are in pain. This can often be heartburn (oesophagitis from oesophageal reflux), abdominal colic (we presume they feel cramps from their bowels, but this has never been proved), or teething (imagine if the roots of four of your teeth all became inflamed at once: the agony!). There are other rare causes.

If we are satisfied the crying is not caused by disease, which is the case in the vast majority of cases, then it is behavioural. But this grand conclusion is of little comfort to the sufferers of the constant crying and lack of sleep. So, what is my advice to you?

First, that there is no harm allowing a baby to cry if you can hack that and want to pursue the controlled-crying approach.

Second, if you feel unable to manage controlled crying and want to resort to bringing the baby into your bed, then that's OK too, but you must take all precautions: lots of space in the bed (which usually means your partner is banished to the couch), not having any alcohol or drugs in your system, no pillows or duvet anywhere near the baby. This does not apply if the baby is under four months, but you can use a bed extender, which means your baby is on a different surface but within easy reach.

Bed sharing over the age four months is not uncommon and the very small risk of sudden infant death is mitigated by the measures I have outlined. The biggest issue is that your baby may end up sharing your bed for a very long time. Babies are creatures of habit and they love contact and security.

The key message, however, if you are struggling with a crying baby, is to seek professional support. We can help you through this. Don't bottle it up, don't try to be brave or stoical.

I want to mention dads here and their role in helping, particularly the scenario of the non-stop crying baby. The majority I see nowadays are super-involved, hands-on, working jointly with the mums to get through the early tricky stages. Sometimes, however, all the pressure falls on the mum (of course there are many single parents who have to carry all the load themselves). One of the starkest examples I have come across was an mother who was exhausted by her baby's constant night-time crying. She was showing clear signs of depression and anxiety and I was worried about her. I asked about the father, who I knew was working from home. But he felt that as the mum was on maternity leave and he was working, childcare was her job. When she asked him for help, he replied: 'I don't have any solutions to your problem.' I reassured her it is a team game, and her problem is his problem too. One person does not make a team. And so I arranged wider-family substitutes to support mum and preserve her mental health and ability to provide the ongoing care for her two children she was desperate to give them.

FEVER

 One of the great fears that parents have is fever, so called fever-phobia. Any time a child gets a fever, the bottle comes out – not the gin, but the paracetamol or ibuprofen. However, it is a myth that a fever in a child requires treatment. It simply doesn't unless the child is showing signs of distress, such as crying, shaking, mottled skin, breathing fast.

Fever will not harm your child. Any complications will be due to the underlying illness, not the fever. And while convulsions with viral-associated fevers are common, they cannot be prevented by keeping the child's temperature down. It is counter-intuitive, but clearly shown by the scientific evidence. Yet, despite all the national and international guidelines and innumerable patient information leaflets on this subject, most parents still hit that paracetamol bottle the moment their child's temperature goes up.

Fortunately, assuming the child is fully immunized, serious illness is much less likely as a cause for a child's fever than it was 20 or 30 years ago. It still does occur, but rarely, for example sepsis caused by urinary tract infections, streptococcal infections which as yet there are no vaccines for, and other rare infections.

IMMUNIZATIONS

 To immunize or not is another dilemma parents face, although their fear is not based on any scientific reason. It stems partly from a basic natural instinct not to want to give your baby drugs or injections, and partly from the huge volume of information that is available on this subject, exacerbated by unfiltered social-media comments and campaigns. It is easy for someone who is a vaccine antagonist to perpetuate inaccurate information without rebuttal, in turn causing those who are vaccine hesitant to step back from the decision to immunize.

There is no grand conspiracy here. Children need to be protected from the 12 important infections that we routinely immunize against, from measles and mumps to polio. Hundreds of millions of children have been vaccinated worldwide without any ill effects, and hundreds of studies have been done confirming the safety of these vaccines. There can be rare side effects, as there always are even from simple drugs like antibiotics, but this is such a tiny number that the benefits of immunization overwhelmingly outweigh them.

HOW TO ACCEPT
THE EXPECTED

Although all mothers-to-be know that when we have a baby there will be a time that we will have to leave them with someone other than ourselves, nothing can prepare us for when it happens. We have created and carried the baby since it was a subdividing cell, it has been totally and completely reliant on us and our bodies and we have given it life for the last nine months. Our hormones and instincts tell us we need to protect this child more than ourselves. Whatever happens, we have to keep them safe.

And then the time comes when you have to leave them, and it's much, much harder than you could have imagined. It is a tidal wave of guilt for leaving them, hormonal pangs of missing them and an overwhelming anxiety and panic that they aren't safe.

What I failed to realize before I was a mother is that your child will always be on your mind. You can still have fun, you can still relax, but it's not in quite the same way as before because you are now accountable for something else and that 'else' depends on you for survival. This was something I wasn't prepared for *at all*. As we had our first child before we were married, we were determined to still have a child-free honeymoon. It seemed like a once-in-a-lifetime moment and perhaps a last-time moment too.

As we sat on the tarmac, about to take off as newlyweds on our honeymoon, I burst into tears. The stress of leaving Parker behind had been building up and I had been trying to push it down and back. I had tried to overcome the sense of terror and fear that engulfed me throughout the days leading up to this moment and suddenly when I realized I couldn't turn back, I was here, on a plane with no exit, it hit me. At a time that we were supposed to be at our happiest, I realized that if we both died Parker would be alone and without parents

We are animals, after all, who want above all else to protect our children.

for the rest of his life. Not only that, but we had made no plans in case this happened, we had left no will or provisional plan for how he would be cared for. No one would know what our wishes were for him. I made Wayne call his lawyer and discuss it with him so there was some form of plan in place. This type of crisis moment is something I had dealt with throughout my life, but I had never been responsible for someone else and this compounded my paranoia and exacerbated my fears to the point of, well, making my husband call a lawyer on his way to his honeymoon. But no one discusses the normality of this.

Our bodies are full of adrenaline and maternal hormones, so of course we have these wild fears and concerns. We are animals, after all, who want above all else to protect our children. I realized in that moment that my life would always now be dedicated to protecting my children. No matter where I went or what happened to me, this would always be my life's priority.

If I'm ever away from the kids for any period of time, Wayne has to constantly remind me that the moment I get home and I've already wiped a few pooey bums, broken up a few arguments, been asked a million questions and dealt with a few tantrums, that I'll be wishing I was back where I was.

But here's the thing,
my children are my point of gravity
even when life is hard,
even in chaos,
even in times of trouble.
They are what hold me to this world.

This also comes with me when I go to work. I always have an internal battle raging, as I want to provide for my family, but I also want to be there for every moment of their lives. If they fall down, who is going to catch them? Will they remember to tell me they fell? What happens if they fall and they think, *Where is Mummy?*

And, ultimately, once you become a mother and you are trying to juggle your needs and those of your family, you can never give any part of your life the full 100 per cent that you want to give it.

HOW TO LET GO

Being a mother is like an endless sea of realizations that come crashing over you. One of these is when you get back from having left your children with someone else to look after them, having worried relentlessly about how they are . . . and you find out they are absolutely fine. And it hurts. Your child is absolutely fine without you and, after the initial excitement of you being home, really couldn't care less where you have been or that you are back with them now.

The first nursery or school drop-off is always an emotional one. I've had the kid that won't let go of you and sobs and sobs as they are dragged away and the kid that walks in without a care in the world.

Both are equally heartbreaking.

Failing and trying, and failing and trying

AKA problems with nursery

The first nursery we sent our eldest to was not a fun experience. It started off great. They came to visit us at home and made us feel really welcome and as though they had his best interests at heart. But on the first day, we arrived and no one had any recollection of him starting there. I was told I wasn't allowed to ease him in and that I needed to leave straight away. By this point, my child was screaming and crying and clinging to me, and I had to leave him and I cried the whole way home.

This continued for the next couple of weeks and my previously happy toddler became clingy and unhappy every time we dropped him off at nursery. He seemed to have become fearful and I couldn't understand why he had changed. Added to which, I had begun to find it hard to sleep because deep down I just knew this place wasn't right for him. It was a maternal instinct but I put it down to me being paranoid and emotional.

One day, Wayne and I dropped him off together and Wayne saw Parker's fear all for himself. We went off and did a few jobs and as we got back in the car, Wayne said, 'Let's just go and get him, it just doesn't feel right.' The relief I felt in that moment was unbelievable. I couldn't get there quickly enough. We picked him up early from the nursery and never went back.

The next nursery was only ever interested in being paid and never provided any updates or information about how he was doing, how he was coping or even what he was up to throughout the day.

Eventually we found the one and it just fitted. He was happy, making friends and the changes in him were all positive. We were kept up to date with how he was getting on and what he was experiencing throughout the week, so we could let him know what was happening each day and it felt as though some stability and positivity had opened up in his life.

Parker's experience with nursery has always filled me with guilt. Putting him in places neither of us were happy with and living with the guilt that I didn't get it right the first time. The truth is, he doesn't remember, and it upsets me more than him. But you learn that is OK too, this is your experience of motherhood, not just of being their mother, and you can have things that mentally upset you that aren't part of their narrative.

Luckily for my next son, all the hard work had been done for him and he also went to the same nursery as Parker and flourished there. When I dropped Carter off for his first day, my experience could not have been more polarized, as he walked into nursery and away from me and never looked back. Leaving me toying with the emotions that he was happy and that was all I could ask for, but also devastated by how he seemed not to need me.

But now I realize I had probably just done my job . . .

There are many transitions in childhood. From home to nursery – to preschool – to high school.

Your children's worlds become more complex. They have to share, learn to queue, have strangers feed them, have to sit, stand, learn to make friends and be a friend. This is where learning empathy is important. Research has shown that using 'reflective messages' helps develop more socially adept children.

This means that parents encourage their child to think about the impact of their behaviour on others, for example, 'When you didn't say hello to grandma, how do you think she felt?' Also, children are encouraged to verbalize their feelings. Showing empathy is encouraging our children to be kind to others.

The best thing that Frankie and Wayne do is spend time with their children. Wayne is fortunate enough to be able to be available to his sons. They play together and Frankie has gained more confidence since having her second son. An involved father is a strong predictor of a child's ability to empathize.

Young children are positively driven to learn. Crawling, standing, walking, feeding, toileting, getting dressed, learning names and so on.

Learning stops being fun at some point as things become more difficult. They compare themselves with each other, but moreover, parents start comparing their child to other children. We need to teach our children that there are many ways to be smart or sporty. We need to avoid determining what is smart/valuable to our children. Teach them to be curious and observant.

We need to help our children learn to answer their own questions or find a way to discover the answer (not just by asking Alexa!).

When my children were young, I used my CBT training with them. When they came home upset if they felt ignored by a friend, I would encourage them to talk about it. We would then try to be curious about why they might have behaved that way. Did the friend do it with other friends?

HOW TO BE ANXIOUS, WITHOUT WORRYING YOU ARE BEING TOO ANXIOUS

From the moment you see that blue line on a pregnancy test, you and your life are changed for ever. Whether that pregnancy ends in loss or a baby, you will never be the same again.

As someone who is highly sensitive to their hormones, I've always known I was pregnant very early on. Everything changes, but also nothing at all. There's no instant bump or feeling, but you do start to mentally prepare and imagine your life with your child in it. From that moment, you are doing everything you can to help this little baby grow inside you, to be as healthy as possible. That includes not eating certain foods, adding foods or supplements, avoiding alcohol or certain activities. For the man, however, I do believe it's slightly different. I'm not taking away the fact that they too imagine and prepare for this new life ahead of them, but it's not physical for them yet. I used to get frustrated with Wayne at the beginning, that our new baby wasn't on his mind 24/7, but then

I realized that nothing had changed for him yet. It's not until this baby is actually here that his life changes. This is now something I always make a point to explain to my expectant friends.

All of this new life comes with its own new anxieties, whether you've suffered with anxiety before or not. There are a lot of doctors that don't make things any easier. There have been many doctors' appointments where I have been made to feel neurotic and stupid for bringing my child in to see them and sometimes maybe they were right, but who knows your baby better than you? No one.

With Parker particularly, my fears ended up being warranted. And that's why I stick to my guns regarding the boys' health. Dr Ed has been a huge help to me, as he's never made me feel that I am over-worrying rather than just being cautious. He has been a pivotal part of Parker's health and wellbeing, but it took a lot of not so helpful and not so kind GPs to get there. There is still this stereotype of the 'first-time mum', which is used in a derogatory manner to dismiss all their worries, fear or terror. How on earth would they feel if after a body-breaking childbirth they were told to go and keep a human alive while being barely able to walk? First-time mothers? More like first-time heroes. Heroes who, among the chaos their bodies are in after childbirth, are learning how to keep their baby alive.

As our roles in this world have changed, I think it is time we stop being reductive about the role of mothers. How about: this world would be nowhere without us. And how would you feel if you'd only had five hours' sleep all week?

PARENTAL ANXIETY

 Parental anxiety is absolutely normal. Not just that, I would worry if I met a parent who was not anxious about their baby or child. It is part of your parental DNA. The issue is when anxiety becomes counterproductive and potentially harmful, both to you and your child.

It is not hard to see how excess anxiety can cause you difficulties, as Frankie highlighted in her book *Open*. My focus here is the impact it may have on your child. Excess parental anxiety may well translate into the child's behaviour – from excess crying and poor feeding as a baby to separation anxiety as a toddler and somatic symptoms of anxiety as a child, such as tension headaches, functional abdominal pain or muscle tics, to list just a few. Children are like sponges, they absorb so much, and initially you may not realize this until the sponge is saturated and the stress starts to ooze out. If parents demonstrate too much fear in a child's formative years, this can certainly have long-term effects and lead to them replicating their parents' behaviour. Chilled parents tend to bring up chilled children.

Now, one of the most potentially adverse consequences of excess parental anxiety is how this influences health professionals and their approach to the child who is having symptoms or who is reported to be having symptoms (these are different scenarios, although equally challenging for a doctor).If we do not identify the underlying cause and recognize that these symptoms are driven by parental anxiety and sometimes in turn, by osmosis, child anxiety, we are in danger of pursuing excessive and unnecessary investigations, putting the child through unpleasant tests and procedures. Even worse, we may well identify an abnormality that is not of clinical relevance but leads to another set of investigations.

Take the case of a child with headaches: the doctor is certain these are stress headaches and confident there is no cause for alarm. The parent is convinced their child has a brain tumour and wants an MRI to rule this out. Now, aside from the fact that if the child is under five they are likely to require a general anaesthetic to undergo the scan, even more challenging is the fact that we then often identify an irrelevant abnormality on the scan, a so-called VOMIT – victim of modern imaging techniques. So, we do the scan, as we cannot persuade the family it is not needed, and we find a congenital abnormality (a brain cyst the child was born with), which is not expected to cause any problems. We have now delivered something for the parents to worry about for the rest of the child's life, and inevitably a repeat MRI will be demanded down the line.

FEAR AND ANXIETY

The symptoms of fear and anxiety can overlap. Fear is a persistent tendency to react in a certain way to a specific threatening stimulus (danger, pain, harm). Anxiety is the emotional state (symptom) in response to a specific stimulus.

Fear is there whether the stimulus is there or not. For example, with a dog phobia, we can still be fearful about dogs without dogs actually being present. We can treat anxiety with medication, among other things. We can't have multiple anxieties because anxiety is a state.

Frankie started to have panic attacks at the thought of going on stage. These were being triggered by a fear of being unable to perform, fear of making a mistake, fear of humiliation (perceived threats). Her brain was telling her to 'run' and 'avoid'. She would sit on the steps near the stage, frozen. I remember speaking to her on the phone when she was on tour. Lots of reassurance, lots of reminders that her panic attack would pass. Lots of building her up and telling her that she could do this.

When Frankie was doing her Sports Relief trek in Namibia in 2020, she had a full-blown panic attack. I had to speak with her on the phone, as she feared failure. Frankie is such a harsh critic of herself that she felt she was letting other people down. Physical exhaustion and high emotions triggered a sense of helplessness and fear. These triggered panic attacks.

Frankie often used to say that she was not good enough for Wayne. That he deserved someone simpler and not someone who struggled with mental-health problems. She feels the same 'shame' and 'guilt' around her children. When she has to take time out, to look after herself and rest, she feels this sense of shame and guilt.

WORRY AND UNCERTAINTY

Frankie would say she was born worrying. Worrying about her parents' safety, sitting on the stairs waiting for them to return. Worrying about something bad happening. We all worry. Sometimes it can be helpful, as it may push us to prepare for something, but that is more problem-solving, which is the helpful part. The problem is that people start believing that worrying is a useful activity and start holding positive beliefs about the function of worry. For example:

Worry shows that I care – about my belongings, home, children, job and so on.

Worry helps me prepare for the worst – rejection, failure.

Worry helps me find solutions.

The key is to try to take a risk and create some flexibility in our thinking and beliefs. For example, Frankie worries that she isn't a good mother or a good singer. If we made a list of what makes a good mother or singer, would worry be included on our list? I don't think so!

Some people think worrying is just plain thinking. It's not. Some people can spend hours just 'thinking' about things in their life. Thinking about not being good enough, being rejected by friends, not working hard enough, thinking they might be a failure. They then follow this with preparing for future rejections, failing and so on.

Frankie had these thoughts at some point in her life. From her teenage years onwards, she didn't feel pretty enough, talented enough, good enough in general. Moreover, she felt that she would be rejected by her friends and colleagues. She would spend time almost preparing for these possible rejections, so that she wouldn't be blindsided by the 'inevitable'. I remember her saying to me, 'I can learn dance routines easily, and that is why I am in the band.'

Characteristics of worry:

- Physical feelings – restlessness, tingling, tight chest.

- Thoughts – I need to be perfect, I can't make a mistake, I will fail, I will be found out.

- Emotions – worrying, sense of dread, nervous, irritable.

- Behaviour – avoidance, looking for reassurance, procrastination.

Uncertainty is a state that most of us find intolerable. We need information in order to gain certainty. People will go to great lengths to speed up or avoid the state of uncertainty.

Worry is a mental attempt to reduce the unknown and feel more certain by thinking through anything that could possibly happen. Worriers constantly ask for reassurance from friends and family. This reassurance does not last long, as they dismiss it and continue with their worry.

Worriers tend to make lists: a simple list, a super list, a holiday list and so on. All because they worry that they will forget. I knew a lady who was a serial list-maker: she even included 'Buy birthday cake' for her one-year-old son. Who would forget such a special day?!

Intolerance of uncertainty is associated with people overestimating that future events will be negative and feeling that they will not be able to cope if the worst happens.

We need to develop a better relationship with uncertainty, which is based on probability, not possibility. We do this by using our rational mind and not our anxious, threat-seeking mind.

Distinguish between hypothetical worries – characterized by 'What if . . . ?' questions – and important real possibilities. Then we can use problem-solving.

HOW TO TRAIN YOURSELF THROUGH GOOGLE

When you're pregnant or have a child, Google becomes your new best friend, for better or for worse. I Googled every little thing. You experience a small spark of joy when you start to type a question into Google and it finishes the sentence for you. It's something so small, but it feels so big: it's the reassurance that someone else out there has asked the exact same question as you, and you realize you are not alone.

When I say I Googled every little thing, I mean every little thing:

Is it normal for them to breathe quickly?

What colour should children's pee be?

How do you know if they need you?

What does normal crying sound like?

Can I . . . ? Should I . . . ?

Sometimes it was helpful, but mostly it wasn't. There seems to be no in-between. It either says they have a deadly illness or there's absolutely nothing wrong with them or you, so step away from the Google search bar.

You can find a lot of information online on parenting forums, and they can be such a brilliant place to read about other mums' experiences, but there is a dark side to them too. Places that were created for us to share our worries and stories in order to help each other can become breeding grounds for negativity and judgement, when really all a parent needs is help and support. Obviously social media can be a brilliant tool, somewhere to share your thoughts, fears and worries with people who will understand without question that nothing is too anxious or too abnormal to ask about.

My children have discovered (far too early) that Mummy doesn't know everything .

Forums and other social media can be super-helpful for learning about sleep training and food ideas, and for giving you the answers to questions you never knew you needed to ask before you had a child. For instance, one of the greatest things I learned was that the only way to help my engorged post-pregnancy breasts dry up was to put cabbage leaves in my bra. And it worked miraculously well!

As my children have grown up in the age of the internet and they have access to modern technology, one thing that doesn't spark joy is the fact they have discovered (far too early) that Mummy doesn't know everything and now tell me to 'Google it'. All thanks to Covid and home schooling, my five- and seven-year-olds now know how much I don't know, and they know that all wisdom is to be found online, not from their parents.

Once I'd had a child, I suddenly had a new-found respect for my parents. Guess what? They didn't know it all and have it all figured out either. They were figuring it out as they went along. Who knew?! I genuinely believed my parents had always been grown-ups and always knew what they were doing. Unfortunately for me, my kids figured out the truth a lot faster than I ever did! I feel we all have things we wish our parents hadn't done or said, and we hold onto some of those things. If they hadn't, psychologists would probably be out of a job.

My approach to Google is simple. Don't. It is a great cause of anxiety and late-night panics. There is no filter, no easy way of knowing if what you are reading is fact or fantasy, subjective or objective, and whether it is of any relevance to your child's symptoms. A good example is when a parent (usually purely coincidentally) notices or feels a swelling in their child's neck. A quick search on Google for neck swelling immediately throws up 'lymph nodes', followed in the next sentence by the word 'cancer'.

While the first part of this search is accurate and most likely the case – what they are feeling is a lymph node – the misleading and terrifying part is the stated cause. Among the 13 million or so children in the UK, there are only 190 cases a year of lymph-node cancer. I see dozens of children with swollen lymph nodes in their necks each year. In more than 25 years, I have encountered around six cases of lymphoma. So, in other words, the likelihood of cancer is incredibly low. But Google suggests otherwise, throwing you into a panic. Don't let it.

HOW AM I MAKING
SO MANY MISTAKES?

Time is not only a great healer, but also a great teacher. Time and experience teach you that you only really learn from your mistakes, never from your successes. You learn that by making errors in judgement or bigger mistakes, your understanding of the world about you grows and with that also comes your sense of confidence. How else are you supposed to figure this whole thing out?

Experience is developed through trial and error. *This* didn't work because of *that*, which means I need to learn how to do *this*, which helps me to discover *that* . . . A journey into discovery doesn't ever begin with success. It begins with missteps into the unknown.

Show me a parent who hasn't put their non-mobile, unable-to-roll-anywhere baby on a bed or a sofa, only to hear a thud, followed by a toe-curling cry which is a strange mixture of pure fear and regret, laced with pride that they've figured out how to roll over and throw themselves onto the floor.

As parents, we try as hard as we possibly can never to mess our kids up. And we worry and agonize over what we have done that might in any way negatively affect them. But really, I believe, we should just aim not to mess them up too much, as it is inevitable that we will say or do something at some point that will stick with them. Perhaps it will affect them and be an unhappy memory, but we can't avoid this entirely. Our children have to learn that we are humans who come into the world, like them, who don't have all the answers, that we fail and make mistakes, which makes it all right if they do the same thing. We have to lead by example and sometimes that example is by not being afraid of doing things wrong and failing. Our children have to learn that no one is perfect, and that no matter how hard we try we can't be the perfect parent to our children. But this also teaches them that they can't be the perfect child to us either. Imperfection is something that makes us all individual and different, and it is something we

I have spent my whole life concentrating on my downfalls, my imperfections. And I do exactly the same as a mother.

should teach our children to make their peace with. And that involves showing them that we fail sometimes. But that we still are loving and learning as parents too, and growing into ourselves.

Whether it's giving them a complex or leaving them in a supermarket or forgetting their coat on a rainy day – the key is not to beat yourself up about it. As long as our children feel loved and supported, they will be able to deal with whatever we, or life, throws at them. And this experience will teach them much more than never experiencing any of the hardships that will, sadly, no matter what we do, come into their lives at some point. We can't protect them from that. But we can prepare them for it.

I have spent my whole life concentrating on my downfalls, my imperfections. And I do exactly the same as a mother. Always telling myself how I should be better, that they would be better off with someone else as their mum, or worrying that they will turn out like me.

I constantly keep a watch for any sign they are going to struggle with their mental health too. Any little worry or deep thought my kids have, I instantly assume they'll be like me. The truth is, if that happens, things have changed so much now and the world is a different and much more open place than it was. The conversation has changed and children are allowed to talk out any complex fears they have lodged inside them. Unlike when I grew up, where all my anxieties seemed to be put down to physical ailments, I believe we would now see beyond the physical and examine the mental struggles that sit behind how they are presenting their 'pain'.

Indeed, my children taught me to encourage them to speak about their feelings. That nothing is too scary or too strange to say. I want them to know no matter how sad or worried they are, nothing will make me stop loving them. That they are perfect because of these imperfections. That it takes the bravest person to say they are scared. That it takes the strongest person to say they feel weak. I want them to know that boys can and should cry, that they should talk about their feelings and worries, that there is nothing to be embarrassed about when airing your worries and that it actually only makes you a better person for doing it. The stereotypes I grew up with should not exist in my children's lives, boys can cry and girls can be strong, and by learning to be more attuned to how they feel and more emotionally responsible for their feelings they will also become more aware of other people's feelings too.

My biggest fear is that my kids will have my brain and my problems with my mental health. My anxiety and depression.

When I was young, my mental health would manifest in stomach aches and breathing struggles. I'd be sent for blood tests, only for them to come back negative and no one any the wiser as to why this was happening to me. Eventually I was given an inhaler for the breathing and my parents were told I was a 'worrier'. And that was that. There was no support given and it kind of became a family joke, that Frankie was a worrier. I don't blame anyone for this, it was the time we lived in. Kids had nothing to be worried, scared or anxious about, right? Now we know that's wrong, these feelings can start from a very young age, and if dealt with early on can hopefully result in them being able to cope and deal with these feelings as they get older. Hopefully not escalating like they did for me. Over the years, as an adult, I've really put in the time to understand and learn how to deal with my mental health, so that I took back the control it had taken away from me for so many years. It's taken me a long time to accept my mental health and that will always be a work in progress, but I'm OK with that. I really hope that by having these conversations with my boys from such a young age, their road to acceptance will be a lot quicker than mine.

THE CHIMP PARADOX

This is the concept developed by psychiatrist Steve Peters about the chimp who is driven by the pleasure principle and instant gratification. He suggests that we need to get our self-esteem from who we are and not what we do (easier said than done, as most of our self-esteem comes from our achievements and our professions) and we need to remeasure ourselves – measure new variables such as integrity, being an honest person and being a good person, which can shift things.

There are three systems in our brain:

The Chimp System Shared with hominoids, emotional, impulsive and lazy, and is with us from birth.

The Human System From ages two to four, our brain learns to use rationality and logic, information and evidence, and empathy.

The Computer System The most important system – for beliefs stored in the system, conscience and empathy.

The first two systems are working together but fighting

each other in the young child. We need to learn how to flick through these three systems.

The Chimp System tells us that we are less than perfect, as we base it purely on success and achievements.

The Human System allows us to forgive ourselves and forgive friends and family because forgiving is a big value. These values give us peace of mind and allow us to accept ourselves.

The Chimp System determines goals. It will chase success, but once it achieves it, it will redefine it – once you get there, it will dismiss it and want something new. It doesn't allow for trial and error, it wants gratification the first time we do something. But we need to allow ourselves to flick into **the Computer System** in motherhood.

HOW TO BE OK WITH MAKING MISTAKES

 The only doctor never to have made a mistake is the one who has never made a decision. The same is true of parents. Only if you take a completely hands-off approach and never get involved in your child's care (which would be the most mahoosive mistake of all) will you not make a mistake.

You are going to make mistakes throughout their childhood, and all the way into their adulthood too. Some you will learn from (that is of course the ideal) but many you will not. As hard as you will try, your filter will fail you, again and again. Your brain will say, *Don't tell them you don't like their new haircut/dress/boyfriend/ girlfriend. . .* but you can't help yourself and blurt out your thoughts, causing immediate catastrophe.

When your children are little, the mistakes you make will be more practical – for example, the first injury because you left your previously immobile baby on the changing mat while you turned around for a second and they decided to show you how clever they are and have learned to roll at this very moment, straight onto the hard floor. Likewise, the hair tongs left to cool down but still within their reach. There are so many hazards, and you cannot negotiate them all without some incident.

After an incident, parents will often end up in the blame game, making a bad situation even worse. We all make mistakes, and just because it happened on one parent's watch this time does not give the other moral superiority as the next time it could well be on theirs. There is no room for smugness or superciliousness here. It is guaranteed to backfire.

Children also need to explore and learn from their own mistakes, the Darwinian principle. You cannot shield and protect your child from every threat. It will not serve them well for their future. This is a hard lesson in parenting.

HOW TO LISTEN
BUT NOT BE TOLD

From the moment you're pregnant, EVERYONE you encounter has an opinion on what you *should* and *shouldn't* do. At first you listen in horror, in admiration, in fear and anxiety to EVERYTHING they have to tell you about their experience and what you need to learn from it. The onslaught is so much that you figure out pretty quickly that only you really know what is best for you and your family.

Until that point, it's really hard not to feel overwhelmed by it all. You are inundated with polarizing accounts of horror and blissful pregnancy/birth stories. Telling someone you were split in half, had an 800-day birth, the baby wasn't breathing and so on and so on can cause an unnecessary amount of stress and anxiety to someone who is either already stressed and anxious, or was enjoying being blissfully unaware of what would happen next. But you are also giving the person a chance to prepare that things may not end up as rosy as they once hoped. This way of speaking is also giving women the chance to be open and honest with each other about the fact that they didn't love the whole experience and found it complex and tricky themselves. Society tells us we have to love every minute of being a parent/pregnant. This leads to mothers feeling unable to speak out about how hard becoming a mother is for your sense of identity, your body and your mind. You feel alone among the sea of happy mothers, happy babies and happy families. Adrift without anyone you can reach out to when you really need to.

As a mother you can't admit aloud a lot of your frustrations, otherwise you could be deemed a bad parent. People jump to the assumption that you don't love your child (which is, of course, ridiculous. If a friend has an argument with their partner, I don't instantly think they don't love them and they are going to break up).

There is then the temptation to act as though everything is fine and perfect, which isolates you from how you really feel even further.

The truth is, we don't want to scare each other, but it's important to know the good, the bad and the ugly. But it should be for each mum to find out for herself and ask the question rather than be told the answer first. We all have different thresholds and fears and there should be a little bit more awareness of how much or how little first-time mothers are exposed to. We need to feel equipped, but also we need to learn for ourselves and we need to let our children teach us. We need to allow women to grow into motherhood and experience the direction it takes them in and the lessons it teaches them rather than instilling them with our journey and our pain.

HOW TO UNDERSTAND EVERY MOTHER IS DIFFERENT (AND HER JOURNEY TO MOTHERHOOD WILL BE TOO)

My sister had fertility issues for around two and a half years, suffering multiple miscarriages, which eventually resulted in her using IVF to have my beautiful twin nephews at the end of 2020. It was an incredibly long and hard journey for her and her husband, on a never-ending rollercoaster of emotions. Having the excitement of being pregnant and then the heartache of it slipping away. Each time, being terrified to embrace any pregnancy for the fear of it being taken away again and again. Having to wait to be given answers as to why this was happening to them. That feeling that her body was failing her. I've met lots of women going through this horrendous ordeal and so many feel that it makes them less of a woman, because their body is made to conceive and carry a baby. As someone who was lucky enough not to experience this, it breaks my heart that this is what they are led to believe. Easy for me to say, I know. But on the outside looking in, there is so much more to a woman than being a vessel for reproduction.

Being my sister's younger sibling with two children of my own instantly made it harder to know what to say when she lost a baby she was carrying. It was always in the back of our minds and incredibly difficult for both of us.

My sister definitely lives by the mantra 'keep calm and carry on'. She's not someone who easily shares her feelings. She's very good at being the life and soul while keeping it all together. So knowing how and when to step in and comfort her was tricky. Also, not to ever forget her husband in any of this. Although it wasn't physically happening to him, the loss of their baby was mentally hard for him too. Seeing my sister go through all this pain, but also mourning the loss of his babies too was devastating.

There is so much more to a woman than being a vessel for reproduction.

Her first miscarriage was a shock to us all, but we were told that miscarriages are common and until you've had at least three, there's nothing to be done about it. It is 'just nature's way'. Which I think makes women feel like they also can't be sad about it because it is normal and natural and part of creation, but the truth is it is devastating and painful. And the aftermath of often having to then give birth to the baby is enough to break anyone, no matter how strong they are. So although these losses are common, we shouldn't be made to feel as though all we need to do now is just move on.

The whole not-telling-people-until-you're-twelve-weeks pregant can make it a lot harder, because although you know that you are pregnant you can't celebrate it with anyone till it's safe, but neither can you let people know what has happened to you if a miscarriage occurs before this three-month window. Just another personal female pain you have to deal with in shame, sadness and guilt. For some, not having to talk about it may help, but for others, dealing with this all alone and feeling unable to open up can be so damaging to their mental health. After all, haven't we been told time and time again that talking to others helps? Especially sharing with other women. That there is no shame about your body not biologically being able to carry on with a pregnancy. You didn't do anything wrong or bad. All growth involves loss.

With my sister's first miscarriage, we all tried to stay positive around her and keep her feeling as though it was only a matter of time, and that this experience was in many ways a part of the process. But I felt unable to read what she really wanted or needed from us. She dealt with it with her usual positive attitude, she accepted it and looked to the future, with the mindset that it would go well next time.

When she was told she was pregnant for the second time, she was living in Bermuda. She tried very hard not to sound too excited and we knew it was because she didn't want to get her and her partner's nor anyone else's hopes up. Knowing what to say was difficult. I didn't want to make her dread the whole thing, but I also understood why it was hard for her to fully embrace it and soak it all in, as she was scared it could end at any moment.

My family and I decided to go and visit her in Bermuda. She had only recently moved there, and we wanted to see where they were living and what their new life looked like. While we were there, she got *the call*.

The doctors told her that for reasons they weren't sure of the pregnancy wasn't progressing in the way it should. I wasn't sure if us being there was a good distraction or a constant reminder that children, like her nephews, were something that she might never be able to have. So all I could do was hug her and hold myself back from saying *it will happen one day*. By now, I wasn't even sure that I did know that it would. She went for her D&C the next day. (Dilation and curettage is a procedure to remove tissue from inside your uterus, which doctors perform to clear the uterine lining after a miscarriage.) The day after, we danced around on the beach, as a family, and drank champagne, knowing that we were all just trying to help her momentarily forget what she had been through and had to face in the next few weeks and months.

Athough these losses are common, we shouldn't be made to feel as though all we need to do now is just move on.

But the third miscarriage was the biggest blow of them all. We were all worried that she wasn't going to be able to take much more. Her mental strength to be able to pick herself up and start all over again must have been wavering and her body had been through so much. The only tiny shimmer of hope was that she would now be able to try to find out some answers for what was going on and why it was happening. Why was this happening to her? This was a question we all wanted an easy answer for too.

I've learned a lot from what she went through about how damaging and heartbreaking it can be to everyone involved and how nothing can prepare you for the shock and fear it fills you with.

But I recall when I was pregnant an assumption was made about me that really wounded me when I least expected it. I was struggling to decide what to have for dinner. I really wanted the steak, but as I enjoy mine medium/rare and had been advised to eat only fully cooked meat, I decided to eat something else. A man on our table seemed to be very offended by this. He couldn't understand how a piece of rare meat could cause any harm to our unborn baby, because 'his mother had smoked thirty cigarettes a day and he turned out fine'. But the truth was that it wasn't the steak that was going to cause an issue, it was that if anything happened to the baby after I'd eaten the meat, no matter how

I will always assume if anything bad happens that I am at fault.

many times I was told that it had nothing to do with whatever had happened to the baby, I would for the rest of my life always be convinced that it was my fault and I would forever blame myself. I am the type of person who has mental-health problems and part of being a mother and being pregnant was always going to involve working out how to do it within that framework. I had to be responsible for myself and also my child, I had to protect us both from my anxieties going into overdrive. And once I became a mother – because that's what you are the minute you're pregnant – I knew that I would always hold myself responsible for things that I couldn't control. And I had to find safeguards to introduce to my life to mediate the potential overwhelm and avoid anything that could trigger panic or self-loathing. I will always assume if anything bad happens that I am at fault.

When we discovered that my eldest, Parker, had asthma and no one on either side of our families suffers from it, I 'knew' it was my fault and that I had given it to him. My logical brain is aware that it's not technically true, but the other part, the part that seems to override everything else, tells me differently, and that is who I am and how I will always be. If I am to be a good mother, I have to know that about myself. There are things that will be outside my control that will happen and I will weaponize them against myself. I have to understand this in order to make peace with the fact I can't control everything and that I can only do my best. The framework for me being a mother is also being a mother who sometimes battles with her mental health and sometimes I need to consider how to take care of both. That sometimes involves less risk-taking and overthinking, but it also means that I am happier and so are my children.

HOW TO TRUST YOURSELF

Always trust your mother's intuition. It is there for a reason. Sometimes we might be wrong, but isn't it best to check, rather than worry about it on our own?

People will force you to question yourself and your parenting, but your child's health, safety and happiness are always at the forefront of your mind and no one should make you feel bad about wanting to protect your child.

When Parker was a baby, his breathing was really fast, especially when he was moving around. I'd always bring it up at doctors' appointments and they would agree but say it was because he had allergies. They weren't wrong about that and there was nothing that needed to be done, but a part of me always felt like they weren't getting to the bottom of whatever was going on. Fast forward to him age seven and, having had many trips to A&E, ambulance rides and hospital stays with croup leading to wheeze, we now know he has asthma and hay fever, and that his reaction to getting ill is usually croup.

So I wasn't wrong: he *was* suffering with an underlying health complaint. And in many ways this gave me confidence to lean into and trust my instincts with my children, because sometimes, just sometimes, I knew what was really going on more than the experts.

My mother's intuition did take a while to kick in, though. Parker was my first child, and having not had much experience with younger siblings or other people's children (because I got pregnant at 24), I had no idea how often babies cried. So I just assumed that all babies cried as much as Parker. After having a few people come round and tell me gently that he did seem to be crying quite a lot, I realized something more was going on. It's funny, isn't it? When you're used to something, you don't see it, because it's your version of normal. But the minute someone from the outside comes in, you realize actually something's not quite right – and I sort of knew it wasn't either, but I didn't want to face it.

Babies are figuring themselves out at the same time as figuring you out, and you are doing the same thing too.

Dr Ed was also the person who noticed Parker's speech was delayed. Again, having no other children to compare him to and being a laid-back parent who wasn't worried about him hitting certain linguistic milestones at particular times, I hadn't worried about his speech. And I hadn't yet developed the confidence as a mother to question it either.

As a mother I think it is important to remember that when you meet another person you don't know them inside out. It takes time to get to know them, and for them to get to know you. You learn each other's likes and dislikes and what works for you both together. So why do we expect any different when we have a baby? Babies are figuring themselves out at the same time as figuring you out, and you are doing the same thing too – you are growing into being their parent and they are growing into being your child.

We teach our trainees never to discount a parent's intuition. Apart from the caveat of the over-anxious or hyper-vigilant parent, if a parent is worried something is wrong, it usually is. There is nothing worse for a parent than having a child who is unwell in their eyes and being told there's nothing to worry about. Parents can leave the consultation feeling patronized, helpless and far from reassured. As medical professionals, we need to read the parents and hear their concerns.

Even if we as doctors are convinced there is no worrying illness present, the minimum we should do is encourage the parents to come back if they remain concerned, that is to say, empower them to feel able to come back and say things are not right. They should not feel that they have to battle the system. Their voices must be heard.

Time and time again, diagnosis is delayed by not paying enough attention to these voices. It is a tricky balance of course, but working with, rather than against, parents and their intuition is vital.

why . . .

WHY DO WE THINK EVERYONE ELSE IS DOING IT BETTER?

Comparison is the thief of joy. There's never been a truer word said. The obvious comparison is the way we look, but I truly believe that comparing ourselves to other parents has become just as big a problem. No matter how many times we are told, we still believe everything in those little squares on our phone is the whole truth and nothing but the truth. We don't scratch beneath the surface. We accept that other parents are doing it better than us and we should feel ashamed for how we come up lacking.

Here's the thing. I don't blame people for only putting up the best version of their lives online for the world to see. Let's be honest, we've done it for years. Why would we 'air our dirty laundry'? We make sure it is scrupulously clean first, as we all race to perfect the imperfect parts of our lives on our social media feeds. It's a vicious cycle, of not wanting to be a part of the problem, but equally wanting the best of your life to be out there because you have worked hard for it and everyone else does it, too. But when do we stop and realize that real happiness cannot be captured in a feed, with a filter on? Happiness is brief and powerful, and so is sadness, which can't be revealed in all its horror. So instead, the world we see on our phones is a version of reality. A reality curated and created to represent our lives, but one that doesn't actually depict what is true. It's just an imitation.

I've spent hours of my life looking at other parents and wondering how they seem to have it all together, and because of this I have tried to make a conscious effort to portray a more realistic version of my life online too. And, of course, people want to see behind the veneer, but by being more open and honest, you also open yourself up to a lot more criticism. And if that involves my kids, I just can't take it. A lot of the performative side of social media is protective because it isn't real, so if it is attacked then you know it is only a creation, not a reality. My advice is to look at people's lives online through the lens of how much you really put up about your life. It is often only the highlights reel. Understand that there is always more going on.

I remember having a conversation with my mother-in-law and she said that when she was a new mother, she would have had no idea how anyone else was doing things on a day-to-day basis, so she never really had anyone to compare anything with. The downside to this is that she would never have really known if someone was struggling either.

I've spent hours of my life looking at other parents and wondering how they seem to have it all together.

As I've said before, I really envy those women who take on the role of the 'stay-at-home mum'. Although I have to say, I don't really like that term. They don't really stay at home at all and I feel it makes the role sound a lot easier than it is. 'Full-time mum' doesn't really work either, because aren't we all? Being home all the time with the kids can be lonely and really hard. It can of course also be rewarding in a lot of ways, but it can be thankless too. I mean, how often did you thank your parents on a daily basis for everything they did for you? We just don't, do we? Everything our parents do, we just expect.

I always carry the guilt that I needed to continue to work. I know for most of us it's just not an option not to. Although with the cost of childcare these days, I'm finding a lot of my friends can't actually afford to go back to work even if they wanted to.

I often find myself going down a rabbit hole of looking at old pictures and videos of the kids and longing for a do-over. I was actually at home quite a lot with them when they were little, but there are big chunks of time that I feel like I wasn't, because I was so busy worrying and trying to do everything I thought I should do that I didn't just enjoy it and soak it all up.

I always look at the mums that cook and bake everything from scratch, always have plans for their kids, play dates, school clubs, always have the right uniform and sports kit on the right day and still manage to have a social life and wear make-up and a decent outfit, and wonder how do they do it?! What we need to do, though, is remind ourselves that we don't know what the rest of their lives are like. Also, maybe they are just naturally organized people – something I have never been. Mainly because most of my life I've just been told what to do on a day-to-day basis.

My point is, there's no such thing as a perfect parent. We need to stop looking at others to see what they're doing and just do the best we can.

It would be great if I could take my own advice, wouldn't it?

It is such a common misconception to think that everyone else is doing better at parenting than you. It is a bit like social anxiety: how come others can walk so confidently into a room while you are clinging firmly to a corner as well as the gin and tonic in your tremoring hand? The answer is they're probably not that confident, but have a different way of coping, using overt and adaptive extroversion, and in the process making you doubt yourself even more. Parenthood can expose, in some, a degree of superiority and even Schadenfreude. There is an innate competitive streak that is unleashed – partly understandable, as you want the absolute best for your child – but some parents find this is most effectively achieved by appearing (even if implicitly) to denigrate the achievements of your child.

Comparisons between children, even within the same family, and even more exemplified by twins, are wholly unhelpful and can be so destructive. Every child is different, they all develop at different rates, and often while appearing to be well ahead in some domains may be behind in others.

It is inevitable that you will feel inadequate as a parent at times. While you will often underestimate your parenting skills, you also need to try to accept that, as humans, we all make mistakes and there will be occasions when that assessment is true. That momentary lapse when you turn your back and the baby rolls on to the floor. There are so many other examples I could give. The still-hot iron left within easy reach, or the tablets where they could be chewed. The car seat on the kitchen counter with the baby still strapped into it (no, never – simply by rocking, the baby can move it to the edge and fall, sustaining a skull fracture).

So, there is no one right way. There are some wrong ways for sure, not many, but some important ones where we do have to direct traffic, but for most part those are intuitive.

Parenting is hard, there is no rule book. Well, there are parenting books – hundreds of them, and websites and forums. If it was easy there would be no need for all this material. As paediatricians we have moved well away from a paternalistic approach, recognizing there is no one-size-fits-all solution to the vast majority of situations.

WHY IS IT SO HARD
TO LEAVE THEM?

Whether it's for a day of work, a night out or a weekend away, leaving my children is something I find very hard. Sometimes they cry and beg me not to leave, other times they couldn't care less and simply wave me off with a big smile on their faces. Both reactions are often equally hurtful. As much as we want them to be OK apart from us, just a little bit of sadness when we leave helps us to understand that they do appreciate us!

We spent a long time weighing up our decision about what to do about our honeymoon. Does Parker come with us? Do we just go for a few days without Parker? Or do we see this as a once-in-a-lifetime moment and go just us two, and really soak up our wedding/ honeymoon experience as a couple, not parents. Both our families were insistent on the latter. Both sets of grandparents shared the care of Parker between them and told us that we will only ever have one honeymoon and to grab the opportunity with both hands and run. So that's what we did. And it was all fine, until we got on the plane. Where I had this sudden realization that if this plane went down, Parker would lose both his parents in one fell swoop. And the panic set in. I burst into tears, my breathing got shallow. Wayne was so confused. Here we were, just married and about to go on our dream honeymoon and his new wife was crying her eyes out. The only way that I could marginally make myself feel better, other than getting off the plane and going home, was to sort our will. I know, what difference would that make? But, in that moment, it was all I could do. Wayne made a quick phone call and made a simple and basic will over the phone, just so we knew where Parker would go and what he would have, if the worst were to happen. To say I instantly relaxed would be a lie, but it is also worth remembering that it's OK to take moments as a couple, or on your own, to be selfish and to do something for you. We all know that happy mum means happy baby and if that's what you need, then do it.

The older the boys get, the harder I find it to leave them. Because they are more aware of what is about to happen, they are either angry that they're not coming with me or sad because they're going to miss us. Even when we go out to dinner these days, they want to come too.

Parker's asthma makes it harder for me to leave as he was in and out of A&E, ambulances and overnight stays in hospital a lot when he was smaller, with bronchitis and croup. But Wayne and I were always there. We still have a monitor in the boys' room and if I'm honest, I'm not sure when I'll ever feel comfortable enough to get rid of it. His attacks in the night come on strongly and without warning, so the thought of not hearing him struggle fills me with fear. I hate the thought of this happening on a night when I'm not there and that he would have to go through it and possibly go to hospital without me.

I had this sudden realization that my son could die in my arms and there was nothing I could do about it.

One night, when Wayne was at a friend's house and Parker was in bed with me, he suddenly sat bolt upright and was unable to breathe and began gasping for air. I rang 111 and she could hear him struggling, so sent an ambulance immediately. Parker was terrified and I was trying to hold him and calm him down, all while falling apart inside. In the moment, because of my own fear and a wash of panic and adrenaline coupled with being woken up in the middle of the night, I suddenly went really lightheaded. I had to lie on the floor, still clinging onto Parker, with my legs in the air, to try to rebalance myself, but it wasn't working. I knew I would be no use if I passed out on the floor, so I rushed downstairs in search of sugar and went back upstairs to the floor with my legs up, downing a sugary drink. Looking back now, I must have looked ridiculous! But in that moment, it was all I could think of to do in order to survive.

I rang Wayne to tell him to rush home, only to call him back to tell him to rush but also drive safely. *So many thoughts and feelings at once.*

The ambulance was taking for ever, so I called 111 back and they were lost! I rang a local friend, who luckily answered his phone in the middle of the night and came to watch Carter for us. I had a moment while I was holding Parker, staring out the window, willing the ambulance to arrive. I had this sudden realization that my son could die in my arms and there was nothing I could do about it. After what felt like hours, the ambulance, our friend and Wayne all arrived at once. It was such a relief to not be alone any more. The paramedic gave Parker oxygen and he started to level out. She said it was one of the worst cases she'd ever seen and he would have to go into hospital to be monitored. The attack meant we were in hospital for a few days, but it's that night that I will never be able to forget.

It definitely plays on my mind when I'm not with him and I will probably always carry the anxiety with me wherever I go. I know I can't live my life in constant fear, but it's hard not to, when you have felt so terrified and so helpless at the same time.

In the past, we have gone out for dinner locally and received a phone call from Wayne's mum telling us that we needed to come home as it had happened again. Imagine if we had been far away, or had had a lot to drink. The fact that it could happen at any point definitely stops me from drinking too much.

Ultimately, I know whoever I leave my kids with, whatever situation is thrown at them, they can cope with it and deal with it, but as a mum, you want to be there yourself. But we can't be there for everything every time, no matter how hard we try, and that's OK.

I know that if I really didn't want to work, technically I wouldn't have to. But I want to support the way we live. And I want to support my family. And myself.

Often, when I look back at when the boys were small, I wish I could do those days again, so that I could be more present and give them every last part of me. But, equally, I'm proud of what I've done and achieved and I hope I instil a strong work ethic into the boys. With every decision comes a cost. If I didn't work, I worry that I would feel worse and that level of sacrifice would be at too great a cost. But on the other hand I wonder if, by not always being there, am I a bad mother? Do they need a better mother?

Sometimes motherhood is about accepting that there will be sacrifices no matter what decision you make.

 This is part of the perfectionist traits of being on overdrive; working long hours to cover up insecurities. Frankie has always worked and feels that if she is not working flat out then she is being lazy and will fail. She will sacrifice pleasure in order to work. It's not always about validation, but a major fear of failing. She is mortified by criticism, but is beginning to feel more confident in herself and her achievements.

 There are many times in a child's life when you may feel sad. Aside from obvious periods when they may be ill, it will often be situations where you have little control. The best example I can give is where your child is not fitting in at school, feels lonely and isolated, or even possibly bullied. You can't force others to be friends with your child, and you can't move them from school to school (occasionally this is needed if the problems in a particular school are irreconcilable). Watching your child suffer when you can do little to help except listen and reassure can be heart-breaking. Most will find their way, however; it just takes one other person in school to bond with your child.

Of course, throughout their life, children will do things and take decisions that make you sad, things you wish they would do differently. The list of scenarios is endless. Remembering your own childhood and young adulthood can help you come to terms with this as it is simply history repeating itself, as it does from generation to generation.

WHY IS THIS SO DIFFERENT FROM HOW I IMAGINED IT?

Overnight, you've gone from being girlfriend and boyfriend, wife and husband, to mother and father. The nine months of pregnancy do not prepare you enough for what is to come.

Neither of you knows what kind of parent you will be until that child arrives – you can try to fathom it out in advance, but nothing really helps as you have to learn on the job. And, of course, you have this clear sense of what kind of parents you are going to be and what kind of parent you are not going to be. *We've all been there, don't act like you haven't.*

We've all sat there, telling ourselves in our heads how we would *never* let our kid get away with this or that.

This is the mother I thought I would be:

My kids will not live on chicken nuggets and chips; they will eat nutritious, healthy food

REALITY – They don't do either, but they live on fish fingers and chips! I try my best to introduce new things, particularly vegetables, but it's a battle.

They will not be allowed iPads at the dinner table, and will do colouring in and other creative activities

REALITY – Any crayons or pencils spent most of the time on the floor and not in their hands. So if we ever wanted to have some nice grown-up time, iPads were the perfect way forward. Please do judge away.

Sweets and chocolate will be for after-dinner only and fruit will always be preferable

REALITY – Fruit is still preferable, but not always possible in practice. Sometimes an easy life is what I need.

I will be a strict parent

REALITY – I still can't stand to see my kids sad or crying, so I buckle under their distress. But it turns out I am a stickler for manners.

I'll always play and encourage outdoor play whenever possible

REALITY – I find playing with the kids so hard, after ten minutes of trying to guess what it is they want the dinosaur to say, I'm bored and so are they. I'm more cuddles and bedtime. Wayne's more Mr Fun. We all have our strengths and weaknesses.

The babies will not have dummies

REALITY – After a few weeks of Parker using me as his dummy, my nipples and I decided enough was enough.

They won't be rocked to sleep

REALITY – Baby number one basically ripped up, screwed up and threw out all my plans from day one. I rocked non-stop.

I will make all my own baby food from scratch

REALITY – This one makes me laugh. If only I had known how fussy Parker was going to be! I started both my boys off with baby-led weaning. But you can't beat a pouch when you're out and about.

Because the truth is, you figure out what kind of parents you are and what roles you are going to play very quickly once you meet your child. It doesn't happen before, no matter how much you try to plan for it. You don't really have the choice to sit around and think about it.

None of these things makes me a bad parent. Although I will tell myself daily that it does. And the only reason that I manage to have moments of knowing that's not true is because I speak about all those things with my friends, and guess what, most of them, if not all of them, experience the same things too!

Of course, your own upbringing has a lot to do with how you parent, and we learn from the good and the bad.

The good things are what we'd like to continue from our own childhood, but equally we do the things that our parents did that we swore we would never do ourselves. But this can be hard when you have a partner who has had a very different upbringing, with different value systems and experiences. How do you work out what takes precedence and whether you should be an anxious parent because that is your predisposition or whether letting go will help you both more?

WHY IS POTTY TRAINING SO HARD?

Seriously, when you think about it, how do you teach someone how to push? I always assumed potty training was just about timing and that all you needed to do was ensure there was always a toilet nearby and were able to get them onto it in time. (A bit like puppy training. How naive I was.) Funnily enough, with Carter, it was that easy – he was using the potty within a week, with hardly any accidents. He was dry and it just naturally happened for him.

For Parker, it wasn't the same. He built up a fear of going to the loo and would just hold it in, to the point of hospitalization. The fear overwhelmed him so much that he had to have a scan, he was just too full. It seems like the most basic and instinctive thing to do – but fears are never logical and they only grow bigger the more people tell you that they don't make sense. We tried therapy, an NHS app and read lots of books on the subject and still nothing seemed to help him push through it. And then one day, out of the blue, he turned a corner and things are so much better now. But it just goes to show again that each child has their own predispositions, battles, mindsets and fears. And as parents we have to learn to listen to them and not find them confusing when they present themselves as illogical and irrational. Potty training is a big step in a child's life as they move towards autonomy and these steps come with fear, and we have to find ways of never expecting things to happen in a certain timeframe or way.

I find teaching them how to blow their nose just as much of a minefield. You can show them, make all the sounds, but how do you explain the sensation? Which speaks to a larger part of being a mother: how do you explain what it will all be like, how it will make them feel? You only know how you experience life and they have to discover things for themselves, with your support, encouragement and patience, and it will be different for every child. You have to sit back and let them discover the world. You can't do it for them, but you can be by their side – waiting to catch them if they fall, are scared or need help.

Why is potty training so hard? My answer here is that it doesn't have to be. I have never seen a child who does not attain continence other than those with severe learning difficulties. So, the issue is timing and, to an extent yet again, the problem of comparisons with others and what parents perceive as the norm.

Generally it will become obvious when children are ready to try the potty. But they need to be ready, and forcing them too early will be counterproductive. Wees are often not so troublesome, but stool withholding is a powerful tool and children can become very proficient at it. It is a vicious cycle as the more they withhold their poo, the harder the poo will be, and the more painful it can be to push out.

Our approach to this, which can help enormously with potty training in general, is to give them a daily stool softener (it comes in a sachet and it is added to water or juice), towards the end of the afternoon. Then the next morning after breakfast have a routine of them sitting on the potty watching their favourite cartoon on a tablet for up to ten minutes. Eventually, as it is so soft, a poo will come out easily, and once this has happened for the first time, the rest is easy. They also need to know you are ambivalent about their failure to poo but give huge rewards when they do it.

CHAPTER 4

what . . .

WHAT ABOUT RULES?

Scheduling your children's day-to-day life helps them feel safe but it isn't reflective of how they will one day have to live with change.

Sleep

This seems to be one of the biggest topics of conversation that every mother discusses with her peers or reads up about from the moment her baby is born. What routine will you put them in? THERE ARE SO MANY DIFFERENT PLANS OUT THERE!

Will they nap in a cot or in their buggy?

Will you be at home for every nap? Or will you try to make them sleep wherever they are?

Will you be with them as they fall asleep?

Will you let them fall asleep alone?

In our family, the strict draconian routine was never going to work. Our lives are anything but nine to five, five days a week, so we can't carve out identical days to slot them in and around at the same time every day. However, we always knew how important it was to encourage good sleep at night, for their sake and our own sanity.

I want to be as open and honest as possible: we were very fortunate to have night-time maternity nurses to help us in those first stages of 'sleep training'. I remember Wayne first mentioning a night nanny to me before we even had kids and I was offended by the idea. It was something that was very common among his peers. (Obviously because they are the small minority of people that can actually afford such a costly luxury.) But I just felt it took away such a big part of being a mother to a newborn and I couldn't see why you would pay someone else to do the night feeds.

But by the time I was pregnant, and after lots of discussions, the idea became a lot more appealing because by this stage I was incredibly anxious about not doing a good enough job. If someone was a specialist in that subject, then I'd rather it was done properly and my self-worth told me that I wouldn't be good enough and my children deserved someone who would be.

I also knew the night feeds would fall entirely on me, and after speaking to Dr Mike McPhillips, my psychiatrist, it was always incredibly clear that in order for me to manage my maternal mental health, I needed to ensure I got enough sleep.

So, I gave in and booked the night nurse. We had about five nights in hospital and then a few nights at home before she came to help. The first few nights of handing over my newborn were really difficult: he was the most precious cargo and we hadn't been separated at night since he was born. As I was breastfeeding at first, she would bring him in when he was due a feed, I would feed him and then hand him back over for the burping and settling back to sleep.

In order for me to manage my maternal mental health, I needed to ensure I got enough sleep.

I know a lot of people will judge me for this decision and that's OK, I was in an incredibly privileged position. But I think it is right and fair that I am honest about the help that I have had, despite the judgement I might receive. It feels like a lose–lose situation. But we all need to be more transparent about the support we need and how we managed it.

Enough of the 'I'm doing fine' while going to the GP to talk about getting myself antidepressants.

Enough of the 'he's doing fine' while I have to have someone help me for the first two weeks of his life because I worried that I wouldn't be able to cope and wouldn't be good enough.

Enough of the 'I have it all and I DO it all'. I don't want any mum reading this to think, how does she do it all? Have a career and be a mum? I have had help and still I battle with it all. Still I feel awful and as though I haven't done it right. If we could all be more transparent, I think it would help us to learn that there isn't a one size fits all. And if we could discuss how hard it is to live up to the expectations we had of what it would be to be a mother, the easier it would be for all of us.

And here's the next truth: as soon as they started teething or got sick or we'd leave home for a night or two, the whole thing would go out the window. Then I'd spend all my time stressing about getting them back into their old routine and feeling like a failure that I couldn't. And it ALL just seemed like much more stress than it was worth.

Now that my boys are older, we don't have a strict night-time routine and that works for all of us. They are always put to bed after their tea and a while before we go to sleep as I know how important sleep is for them. But we have had our boys in and out of our bed with us for years and at times it's not the most comfortable, but I wouldn't change it for the world. I know how much I hated sleeping alone when I was a child and how scared and overwhelmed by it I often felt. It was often the time when my fears would develop and take hold of my mind. So we let them into our bed in the night if they are scared or nervous.

THE IMPORTANCE OF SLEEP

Many of my clients with general anxiety will at some point worry about their sleep. Sleep plays an important part in our mental health and wellbeing, and needs to be taken seriously.

All animals sleep, so we know that sleep has a vital function – we may be immobile, with our eyes closed, but our brain activity is very complex while we are asleep. A major function of sleep is to transfer memories from the day to the long-term filing cabinets of our mind. A clear-out of memories also takes place. Sleep is as essential as breathing, and many would argue that if we just let our body do what it does, sleep would return to us. I often tell my clients that sleep is about surrender, whereas people who struggle with sleep do the exact opposite. It becomes an obsession, a battle. Unfortunately, the more we fantasize about having a restful and life-affirming sleep, the more it can elude us.

There is a whole industry out there, seducing us with products to help us sleep – CBD is just the latest product being toted around as a treatment for insomnia – many others are available. Insomnia can result in problems with concentration and impact your mood, as well as causing you to worry.

The signs of insomnia disorder are:

- Sleep problems three nights a week and going on for at least three months.

- Sleep problems occur despite having enough opportunity to sleep

- Difficulty initiating sleep

- Difficulty maintaining sleep

- Early-morning awakening

- Sleep disturbance causes clinically significant distress or impairment in social, occupational, educational, academic and behavioural functioning

How much sleep do we need? We often think there is one number of hours that is right for everyone. There's not. There is a range. In the UK the average sleep time is 6.8 hours per night, but some people need more, some less. In order to improve our sleep and its patterns, we need to work with our own nature and circadian rhythms. Some of us are larks and others owls, but most of us are somewhere in between these two sleep profiles. There is also always a difference between the objective and subjective assessment of sleep quality by an individual.

When it comes to sleep problems, cognitive reframing can be a useful tool. We don't expect to be able to concentrate for an uninterrupted 6–8 hour stretch in the day, but we do expect our sleep to be like this, which is unrealistic. We beat ourselves up for waking up in the night, we overthink the gaps in our sleep and start worrying about it during the day. What would we do if our concentration was interrupted in the day? We'd take a break and then carry on with what we were doing. We can take this approach to our sleep, too. It's OK to be awake sometimes during the night – try not to overthink it.

Sleep involves the interaction of two factors:

1. Circadian (master-clock) factor

2. Wake/sleep history – the longer you stay awake, the greater your need to sleep

How can we learn to sleep well again? By trial and error and trusting ourselves to figure it out. Babies can do it and so can adults! Some techniques include stimulus control – restricting time spent in bed – and paradoxical interventions – telling ourselves to stay up all night. It's also important to develop good 'sleep hygiene' habits:

• Strengthen your connection between sleep and bed

- Get to know your circadian rhythm

- Don't go to bed with loose ends – put the day to rest. Try to wind down by rehearsing 'What am I doing tomorrow?'

- Create a transition or distinct marker that helps you tell yourself every night that this is now bedtime. Our body needs a rhythm, so this maker lets our body expect sleep next.

- Sleep stopping distance – decelerate slowly as you approach bedtime. Avoid re-alerting activities, like exercise, which can be stimulating

- 'Me time' – take a bath, relax, try to have a nice evening and recognize the signs of sleepiness

To treat insomnia, try resetting your sleep instinct. For two weeks, go to bed at 1am and get up at 6am. You have to wake up at this time every day – if you don't sleep, unfortunately you still have to get up. There can be no napping during the day, no lying on the bed – your bed has to be only associated with sleeping at night. Although this is exhausting, by narrowing the sleep window to five hours, we can reset our sleep instinct. We will start to sleep more during those five hours and then gradually we can increase that sleep window.

CHILDREN AND NIGHTMARES

In order to try to decrease the possibility of nightmares, create a safe environment before children go to sleep, avoiding high levels of stimulation before bedtime.

If they wake up from a bad dream, remind them that the dream is over, and help them to ground themselves. They could leave a reassuring note for themselves by their bed, for example.

One very powerful technique that removes a lot of the fear associated with nightmares is imagery rescripting – changing the dream ending during the day. For example, if a scary clown is chasing you in your dream, imagine taking the mask off to see that really it is your friend.

CHILDREN IN OUR BEDS

Frankie and Wayne struggled to get Parker out of their bed and into his. Even if he went to sleep in his own bed, he would find his way back to theirs, because he found it difficult to put himself back to sleep if he woke up in the night. This is a battle that most parents have to engage in at some point (unless you have an angelic baby who has been programmed from day one!).

I remember Frankie and I talking about engaging him in buying his new grown-up bed, helping with putting it together and so on, so that he had some ownership around it. However, it might take many attempts to establish a new routine where a child sleeps and stays in their bed all night. If the child learns that he needs our presence to fall asleep, then he needs us to be there when he wakes up in the night, too.

Habits take time to form. The most important aspect is consistency. Every day, establish the same bed time routine. Babies and adults alike love routine: it is comforting and makes us feel safe and loved.

Eating together

I have always felt a huge pressure to eat as a family round the dinner table every night. When I was younger, it would only really happen on weekends as my dad wouldn't be back from work often during the week. But there is a model-family image, isn't there, of a family chatting about their day at mealtimes.

While the boys are still small, they need to eat earlier than Wayne and me, and I just don't think it makes sense for us to be eating that early! And life just isn't how it used to be for most families. It's not always that straightforward. I don't know many families that are all in the same place at the same time, every day, without exception. But I have always felt so guilty about it, so I asked a child psychologist how important eating together was and he told me that he only manages *at most* two nights a week with his own family. Hearing him say this instantly removed that sting of guilt I'd been harbouring all this time.

I don't disregard any medical or psychologist advice on any of these subjects. I am fully aware that children need and like routine, but it's just not always realistic and I hate the pressure and guilt that it puts onto mothers. Our lives are all different and we have to do what works. And that doesn't mean we are doing it right, it means we are doing what is right for us and our family.

 Remember to encourage your child to play outside and try not to over-schedule their day.

We have to set realistic goals. I don't want to keep my children waiting past their dinner time for Mum or Dad to come back. I don't want them to feel as though they have failed because they still get scared in the middle of the night. Or that they aren't fitting into the schedule that I have made for them to fit into. I don't want to set them up to fail, or us to fail them, I want us to all try to do our best. And accept when things don't go right, just the way we accept when things do go to plan.

This box-ticking at school is also something I find hard to tolerate with my kids. Especially having a child that needed extra help, who is now definitely not top of the class but is totally capable and able – it just didn't come until a little later than it did with some of his peers. Why is everyone expected to get to the same level at the same time? Exams seem like an unfair and inaccurate way to judge how intelligent a person is. Some people perform amazingly under pressure, others crumble and fall apart, so why is a child's whole life (which is what we are led to believe) completely hanging on this one exam?

 Structure is important in children's lives, and this is maybe a better way of framing this topic than 'rules'. Mealtimes, bedtime, similar time for baths, etc. are all important to teach children about routine. Without this, anarchy reigns and behavioural problems become more likely. They need to know boundaries, and of course they must learn about danger and behaviour that is unacceptable, such as biting. At the same time, they do need freedom, the opportunity to make their own mistakes and learn not to repeat them. Using the iron example, a toddler will learn after the first time they touch a hot iron.

How parents will parent is a personal choice, and again I would never direct. There are so many factors that inform their style, including, and quite powerfully, their own parents' methods when they were growing up. Some are super-relaxed and lenient (which can lead to a manipulative child who does not understand boundaries) and others are strict disciplinarians (which can lead to push-back, rebellion and constant mayhem). As with everything in life, a balance between these two ends of the spectrum is likely to be the best approach.

It is important not to spend the day telling your child off. This loses currency quickly and induces antipathy towards your castigation. The child will often push even further to get a reaction, and the situation can descend into a daily pattern of screaming and negative energy. For every time a child is being told not to do something, there should be many more times they are being given positive encouragement and praise. As in the workplace, praise yields better performance, whereas constant negative feedback brings out the worst. This change in approach can be hard.

Many children use food as a weapon. This can drive parents wild, trying desperately to persuade their child to eat as they fear long-term consequences on their growth and development without adequate nutrition. We see à la carte menus appearing, iPads at the table, all sorts of entertainment, and the child still refuses to eat.

Our approach is clear and can seem counter-intuitive. But it works. There is one family meal, and unless the child needs a special separate meal because of allergies for example, then they get offered the same meal. If they don't eat, they don't eat. They will never, ever starve themselves. Eventually they will eat. It requires nerves of steel from the parents. I know that advice again is cheap. And I am writing this as I have just got the dog to eat lunch by trying three different meals as he refused the first two. Epic failure on my part, and so I am writing this section with a feeling of guilt and hypocrisy! But doctors generally don't take their own advice, so that's OK then.

WHAT MAKES IT SO HARD?

Am I the only woman who had a baby and only then did it dawn on me that I now had to teach this tiny human everything they needed to know to turn into a well-rounded person? Morals. Manners.

How to be kind

How to be good

How to be considerate

How to be patient

How to be compassionate

How to make others happy

How to be generous

How to be humble

How to be fair

How to be openhearted

How to be open to change

How to embrace difference

How to see beyond your own life
experience

How to feel empathy

How to feel love

How to give love

How to eat properly

How to blow your nose

How to go to the loo

How to sleep

How to listen

How to learn

How to be HUMAN

(When sometimes I don't even know how to be a fully
functioning human myself!)

WHAT ABOUT SCHOOL?

We all like to think that everything we teach our children sticks. My biggest disappointment is if I ever hear one of my boys say or do something unkind. If they didn't get ten out of ten in a test at school, at least they've tried. But if they're not kind, that's a harder hurdle to overcome.

There have been many times recently that my youngest has corrected me. He's been learning about right and wrong, good and bad decisions, and their consequences. And I have to say, I definitely feel judged. I'm the mum that brings a treat at the end of school, be it chocolate or a cake. Recently, Carter informed me that he didn't want his chocolate buttons as they are unhealthy and would instead like some grapes. He then had a burger for dinner another night and told me he would eat it that night, but that he wouldn't have one every night as that's unhealthy. They both always tell me off for leaving the tap running while they clean their teeth! I like to feel that, in general, these days we all know more about health and the world in order to live a better and longer life. They clearly know more about right and wrong in that aspect than we ever did at their age. But teaching them right from wrong in a social situation can be a lot harder.

Letting them be sensitive and able to compromise, but also be strong enough and confident enough to be able to hold their ground in certain situations is just as important. All we can do as parents is have those conversations and try to lead by example. The need to fit in with peers is something we've all experienced and still do as adults. And it tends to be my biggest worry for my kids. I will obviously teach my boys that drugs are unsafe and not to do them. But when they're out with their friends, will they have the strength to say no and walk away? The same goes for bullying. I often feel like kids get dragged into situations in order to fit in. I want them to know that it's wrong and that the damage to that one child will be much greater than the damage to their popularity and that those friends aren't worth it. So much of what our children will do is out of our hands. So all we can do is do our best, have those important conversations and pick up the pieces or help them to make things right and not do it again when something goes wrong.

Children spend up to 40 hours a week in school, away from you. You know little of what goes on there, apart from what they may tell you (even that may not be an accurate reflection), and what you may find out at parents' evening (which often appears even less accurate – why are they telling me my child is being rude, or not paying attention? Just not possible!). Teachers say that parents' evenings for them can at times be like sniper's alley, with them cowering behind a child-sized desk, trying to dodge the marauding parent who is determined to find that teacher who did not give their child an A for their coursework. And any failures must be the teacher's, not their child's.

As 2020 demonstrated, with most classes being virtual or self-directed, with parents having to do the teaching, education is a real challenge. Probably because of COVID-19, more parents appreciate just how hard a job teachers have. Every parent wants to see their child reach their maximum potential. The problem is that does not mean every child will get an A. The normal distribution curve of childhood height and weight is also applicable to educational attainment. Intelligence alone does not equate directly to performance, of course. Many factors will affect how well a child does, in addition to their innate intelligence: the quality of the teaching, the environment, the success of their social interaction and integration, their happiness and stability within the home environment all have an impact.

WHAT IF THEY BECOME LIKE ME?

I have spent most of my time as a mother hoping that my kids only get my good parts. The last thing I have ever wanted is for them to have my anxious and depressive brain.

I try so hard to teach my boys that all feelings are warranted and valuable – that they shouldn't feel scared or anxious about any of the feelings they feel, that they all fall on the spectrum of normal. I want them to know that they can always express their feelings without any judgement and to listen to others with the same sensitivity. As someone who has suffered with mental health all my life, I try my best to remember what didn't work for me as a child and avoid re-enacting those behaviours.

For example, if I was scared of something when I was younger and was told *'It's OK and we won't let anything happen to you'*,

I did not feel better or less scared.

So instead, when one of my children presents their fear to me, I talk it through with them and address it, rather than brush it to one side, so that they know I take them and their concerns seriously. That nothing is too childish or too scary to not come to me with – that any concern they have is enough of a concern for us to speak through together and discuss the best ways we can go about handling it and dealing with it. My ambition is to constantly prove to them that I will always be there to listen to them, no matter how big or small their worries or fears are. I don't want them to ever keep things bottled up inside. That the superpower with anything is talking it through and out loud. That once it isn't locked inside them it becomes less scary and they don't have to face it and try to minimize it alone.

 When my children were young, I used my CBT training with them. When they came home upset if they felt ignored by a friend, I would encourage them to talk about it. We would then try to be curious why they could have behaved that way. Did the friend do it with other friends?

I've tried all sorts of things with the boys and their worries. I even tried a practice called 'the worry monsters', which is a cuddly toy: they write their worry down, put it in the monster's mouth, zip it up, go to sleep and in the morning their worry will be gone. But my boys had lots of practical questions about how it works and where their worries actually go. So when trying to teach them about it, I managed to get myself involved in this elaborate story of the monster eating the worry and digesting it for them. Except both the boys woke up and told me they were still worried about the same thing and that the monster hadn't eaten their worries at all.

It forced me to realize although this may work for other people's children, it didn't work for mine because they needed to talk it all through first as they couldn't let it go until they had begun to rationalize it with me. Children are so much more like us than we give them credit for, their concerns and anxieties live on and grow bigger just like us adults. I should know: I can be worrying about something for weeks in my head and it's not until I say it out loud that I realize how illogical it is. So why would I expect anything different from my boys?

My ambition is to constantly prove to my children that I will always be there to listen to them, no matter how big or small their worries or fears are.

When I was younger, I was terrified of death (and I still am) and this is also Parker's main worry. I think for all children it is one of the greatest and most complicated things to come to terms with because it defies so much of our living logic. Where do they go? What happens to them? Do they live on? How does it happen? Why does it happen? And, of course, I don't have any answers – no one does. So when it comes to the answers, I find it really difficult to provide the truth without terrifying them. Ultimately we all have to find our own way of making our peace with death as an inevitable part of living and find a way of accepting that.

I have found it particularly interesting to see how differently my two boys feel about death. Parker is worried about being alone and hates the unknown of what happens to him when he dies. Carter, on the other hand, is totally unfazed. He has all the answers. Apparently he'll go back in my tummy and then come back out as a baby again. Or he and Parker can write to Santa and he'll bring me back. Or his aunt and uncle will come and look after them.

How different can two kids be?

Ultimately, we all have to accept the things we cannot change, and if they do grow up and have aspects of my mental health, then that is the way they are and a deep part of who they are. There is nothing I can do to change that, but I can make it less scary for them and let them know I am always here to talk everything through and that I will love them no matter what or who they are.

A lot of being a mother is accepting that you can only do so much. That you can't change the inevitable or intrinsic no matter how much you want to. You too have to find your peace with things not going how you would want them, and that of course all you want is their happiness but with that comes accepting their unhappiness too. And one day there will come a time when you have done the best you can do, and they will have to live without you.

○ Frankie's anxiety takes the form of avoidance on most things as she feels that she can't achieve anything and will fail anyhow. She worried as a child. Nature and nurture will tell us that at least one of her boys will struggle.

Research tells us that infants actively look at their caregivers for emotional information to appraise an uncertain situation (social referencing). This is how children learn phobias vicariously. Moreover, maternal modelling of pain behaviour has also been shown to be learned by the child. This is relevant for needle phobias, as children are expected to be vaccinated extensively in their early days. In fact, negative information about anything – food, hospitals, animals, school and so on – has been shown to lead to the development of fears and phobias.

Exposure therapy is a very useful strategy for dealing with social anxiety and phobias. The child is introduced to the feared object (for example his new bed or nursery) in incremental, manageable steps (the ladder of fear). Exposure therapy works on the basis that if we are exposed to the feared object in bite-size pieces, then we learn to tolerate distress/anxiety but, more importantly, to reappraise the feared object. We might predict that the scary dog is a killer (rate fear 10 out of 10), and then re-rate the scary dog after seeing a picture of him (fear 6 out of 10). We could then look at pictures of several dogs, and then a video, then take a walk in the park with a friend's dog on a lead and so on. Fear is a sensation that will reduce over time and children learn a sense of mastery. Common fears in early childhood include storms, heights, the dark and blood.

I have always encouraged Frankie to speak to her children about anxiety and to 'normalize' it to some extent. Let them talk about their worries, give the 'worry voice' a name so that the child can observe it as a separate entity. This is far healthier than a child worrying about it privately and planning to avoid it last minute.

We have spent many sessions where Frankie blames herself for the anxiety in her son. She feels helpless at times, angry at times, but mostly protective.

She is a good, warm, attentive parent and her sons are very close to her. They see her challenging herself by taking on new challenges and can see that we can overcome fears.

WHAT DID I EXPECT?

As a mother, I feel a really common mistake all mothers have made is to neglect and sacrifice themselves to the point of breaking, so that they can give every last part of themselves and their life to their children. I see it all the time. We feel selfish for taking any time for ourselves. But if we aren't happy, fulfilled, well-rested women, how do we expect to be the best parent we can be to our children? And how do we expect them to learn that self-care and boundaries are incredibly important too? This involves sacrificing some of the dreams we had envisaged when we embarked on this wild and beautiful journey. We can't live on projections of who we are or who our kids will be. We have to live with what we have and make sure we leave room for both of us to grow into ourselves.

When we decide to have children, we can't help but imagine what their lives might be like. And sometimes, as they get older, the lives we have imagined for them might need to change. Our expectation of what will make them happy might not be what will actually make them happy in reality. And what makes us happy isn't actually what we thought it would be either. And we have to let go of who we thought we would be and, equally, who they would be.

I met a woman whose son tried to take his own life in his teens and I remember she mentioned a time when he was a toddler and she was having a conversation with him about what he would be when he grew up and he said he just wanted to be happy, like the man mowing the lawn, and she replied saying that didn't he realize he could be anything in the world, like an astronaut or a doctor? At the time, she felt as though she was trying to instil in him that the world was his oyster and that he could literally do whatever he wanted with his life and she believed in him. But after he had tried to commit suicide, she felt awful because she realized all she wanted for him in his precious life was to be happy, she didn't care how successful he was or what job he had. The only thing she longed for with all her fibre was his *happiness*.

This struck such a chord with me. As I am also guilty of wanting my children to know that they can become anything they want and that we believe in them and will support them through it all. But maybe there's something in letting them know that smaller goals can sometimes be the biggest goal of all, happiness?

The path to happiness isn't success or a realized dream. That is just an addition. Instead, real and lasting happiness can't be found: it has to be fostered inside you.

This is such a hard one. In essence, no one can make another person happy. You can try to ensure that your child is supported, loved and encouraged, and hope that this will be enough for your child to be happy. One thing we do know, material endowment (and particularly excess) is not the way to ensure their happiness. In fact, the opposite outcome often occurs.

I have seen this so many times: wealthy parents who give their children everything they could possibly want, yet they end up unhappy, and this sometimes leads to self-destructive behaviour and mental-health problems. On some occasions it is because the material gifts have been a substitute for parental presence and love. But not always. That is not to say children should not be treated to things.

Of course, sometimes support, love and encouragement are still not enough. So many other external factors can influence a child's happiness, including school, friendships and sometimes quite deep issues that they simply won't tell you about, such as struggles with their identity and sexuality.

WHAT DO I LET THEM SORT OUT FOR THEMSELVES?

We all do our best to protect our children from all the terrible things that life brings, be that physical pain, the hardship of the world or the cruelty of people, but we know it's not realistic to bring them up unaware that these things are a part of living.

We all know that we grow and learn through the hard things that happen in our life. I want my children to be able to cope in those situations and not be overwhelmed when things go wrong. To be ready to accept the rough as well as the smooth. I believe it will serve them well to know that not everything will look like perfect happiness, but it also won't look like perfect unhappiness either. With life there is, and always will be, an element of trial and error.

When I was at primary school, I remember being angry and frustrated at my mum for not being the type of parent that came down to the school every time I had an argument or a falling out, like some of the other mums. But since becoming a mother myself,

I realize that she was right to let me fight my battles without her, because it taught me I could, and how to stand on my own two feet when I needed to as well as accept when I could have done better and shouldn't have behaved in a certain way. I'm glad that she left me to navigate this new landscape for myself, as I needed to figure it out. And by doing so, she allowed me to make independent judgements.

I try to do the same with my children, despite my first instinct being to jump in and fix anything and everything that happens to my boys that they don't like, because how will they ever learn to solve these problems in the real world, if I don't let them?

I had always felt it was very important for the boys to never see Wayne and me argue. And to be honest, it doesn't happen very often. I am not confrontational and would rather have a conversation about something when we've both calmed down a bit, and I always felt that was the only way to be, for our children to never see us disagree. But after having a conversation with a friend, she told me that her partner is physically unable to handle an argument or a disagreement and feels it's the end every time they have a small spat, because he never saw his own parents argue. So, obviously seeing your parents shouting and screaming at each other is not healthy, but seeing them disagree and then find ways around it to compromise surely teaches children how to communicate well and that disagreeing is part of experiencing someone's lived reality.

WHAT IF I JUST IGNORE EVERYONE ELSE?

What if we all stopped thinking about what everyone else is doing?

What if what everyone is telling us is actually the wrong way to live our lives ?

What if we just lived?

No matter what kind of parent you are, it is hard to be immune from the pressure of what you should apparently be doing. You are given all these goals and targets.

- Breastfeed the baby for 6–12 months

- The baby should be crawling before they are eight months old

- They should be walking by the time they are one year old

- You should have them potty trained before they go
  to nursery

- They should probably be able to speak two languages

- The toddler should be socializing and making friends

- The toddler should be sleeping all night and dry

- The child should be able to count from 1 to 100

- The child should have found a hobby that they love

- The parent should love every moment

- The parent should be able to do it all

- The family should eat dinner together every night

- The family should always be happy

But when we set these time limits and rules on ourselves, we miss out on the process and the journey of growth that happens in between these big moments. Often it is these small moments that hold so much magic and brilliance, and we don't value them as much because they aren't an 'achievement'. An achievement for whom, though? You are the parent, you are the mother, this is your life, your experience. Perhaps being a mother is actually about knowing the basic expectations but realizing that not each child will fit these patterns and development cycles and that they are growing in a slightly different direction, that they are reaching for a different light from the one society recognizes as the spotlight . . .

I hugely struggled with this development expectation with a child who needed extra help with speech. There was so much frustration with being unable to communicate. He was frustrated that I couldn't understand what he needed, and so was I. If we hadn't put such a huge amount of pressure on ourselves, perhaps it wouldn't have built up until he had complete meltdowns. Perhaps we wouldn't have felt so terribly guilty because we couldn't understand him in his times of need. I think the truth is that he felt our concern that he wasn't achieving this quantifiable 'thing' and it upset him even further and made it ever harder for him and for us.

Tantrums

Don't be that mother who watches someone else's child have a meltdown and judges them and their parents. It's always more complex than you realize. Maybe they haven't yet found a way to communicate. Believe me, that parent is feeling all the shame and embarrassment enough for everyone in that

Shop
Park
Nursery
Restaurant
Train
Taxi
Party
Library

Tantrums are a part of growing up. They are a form of expression. However uncomfortable it might be for you to hear, that mother feels worse. She feels your judgement and she is already giving herself hell.

HOW TO DEAL WITH TANTRUMS

Nothing can prepare you for the toddler tantrums. The volcanic eruptions over even the most trivial of issues are frightening and perplexing in equal measure. Most parents will fight fire with fire (well, after the almost always futile attempts to de-escalate the situation by trying to reason with the offender). No matter how much you shout back, you will never win. This requires a different strategy. It works, but it is difficult to implement and sometimes not appropriate.

The technique involves walking away, which is fine at home, but clearly will not work in a supermarket. Offering your child up in lieu of paying for the now 12 bottles of Beaujolais (it was six before the tantrum) is unlikely to succeed. However, at home, walking away is the best option. Walk away, don't engage, leave them on the floor screaming (if need be, place them in a safer environment if you have precious china or glassware within a little arm's length). Go to your bedroom. Take time out. Sit on the naughty step if you want (no point getting the toddler to do it, because it won't work and reinforces attention, which they crave). If you cut off the oxygen of a response and show complete indifference, it can pay dividends. It is of course not a panacea, and there are times when you simply have to follow commands, like allowing them to go to nursery without putting their shoes on (a favourite ruse). But they will eventually learn not to act up if they get nothing back from you.

This is equally true of young adults, where there can be a battleground and you may be dealing with someone much bigger than you. Just get out of the house when they kick off. When they have calmed down, then attempt a debrief, always trying to remain calm and talking in a low voice, replaying what happened, what triggered it and how they (and you) reacted. Sometimes you will also learn lessons about your own responses.

We've found the school system hard as it only reinforces those quantifiable steps each child is meant to take at the same age. How can it all be reduced to every single human performing in the same way when we know that we are all different with different needs and skillsets? All children are expected to reach a certain level at the same time and it's just not realistic. While I understand there has to be some type of a benchmark, sometimes it just seems too outdated to approach things by scoring someone against their peer. What if a child is better at different things than the ones they are marked on at school? Surely those qualities are also important?

Carter was held back a year to repeat reception. As the youngest in his year, an August baby, he was struggling to keep up with the other children in the class. I felt I had failed him. All those times while I was pregnant with him, when people were telling me to 'cross my legs' to keep him in till September, they were right. I never knew what an impact being the youngest would have on him. Holding him back a year was such a tough decision to make, but also one I felt as though we should have been made more aware of before. As, of course, there is always going to be the youngest kid in every year, so surely their journey or approach to education should be slightly different for them?

Children begin school at such a young age in the UK. I often wonder if they did start slightly later, as they do in many other countries, whether it would be better for their growth and individual development rather than mass development. I believe they need more time to just be children and play and grow and experience the world first before we expect them to learn what we think they should.

WHAT IF I LET GO OF CONTROL?

Wouldn't our lives be so much easier if we just accepted that we can't control everything? I know my life would be. Most of my stress and anxiety comes from not being able to control life. So why do I still insist on trying to?

I hope the pandemic has taught us that we can work as hard as we want, build the life that we envisioned, but there will always be things that happen that can change everything that is bigger than us. Life throws us curve balls all the time and all we can do is ride the wave as best we can without feeling too fearful that we don't have control of when it comes but we can decide how we want to navigate it.

The same goes for our kids. We can plan their path, protect them as much as possible, but they will inevitably make decisions we don't like and make mistakes, and all we can do is guide them through life as best we can.

And by trying to prevent them from making mistakes, we are only teaching them to internalize them when they do.

WHAT IS NORMAL?

For most people, normal is a goal to work towards.

But what is normal?

It's different for us all.

Why do we spend so much of our lives trying to fit in and expecting our children to do the same? If anything, I'm more proud of my boys when they go against the grain. I don't want them to feel like they always have to fit into a certain box and I want them to have freedom of self-expression, of independent thought, of not fitting in because they feel they have to, of exploring who they really are rather than who the world tells them to be.

When I was younger, popularity was the goal and being liked by everyone was the ultimate success, probably because deep down I felt as though there was something deeply wrong with me, so I figured if I was accepted and loved, then that would take away my problems.

Now that I'm older, I hope my kids aren't the popular ones. I don't want them to have the pressure to conform or to feel they need to please everyone at such a young age. I want them just to be. I spent my life as a people-pleaser and it has served everyone else but me. Yes, you need to learn to compromise and to work and deal with other people and to sometimes do things you don't want to do, but not in every area of your life.

I spent my life trying to act 'normal' and to be who others wanted me to be, because I thought it would make things right. And it didn't and things went really wrong. I had become a persona rather than myself, and because I sacrificed what I wanted and needed for the sake of what others wanted, I went down a very dark path. I now know that I can't do the same as a mother, I can't become the character of a mum that society has told me to be. I have to live a full, authentic and joined-up life where I accept my limitations. I have to find a way of not letting too many people tell me who I should be or what I should be doing. I can't live that existence again. I had to learn the hard way to find that some boundaries are not to be crossed. I won't do it again and I don't want it for my children either.

Because, ultimately, what is normal for you? As mothers we are told that normal is constant pure joy and happiness, but it's hard work and lonely. This does not mean that we love our children any less, that we are abnormal mothers. We don't expect to be the best at everything in life, so why is motherhood different?

231

Surely your own normal is normal? And staying true to that is absolutely the best and most important thing to do. For me, normal is being happy, but also having bouts of depression and sadness. Accepting that and understanding that is NORMAL has allowed me to be the best mother I can.

It may not look like what normal is for everyone else or even for you, so perhaps you should ask yourself what is your normal? Lean into that, sit with it, consider it and come to terms that that is the way it is and that is what makes you you and me me.

Normal is you.

 A 'normal' childhood is often referred to as the best foundation for a child, as if there is a clear definition of what this means. In this context there is no such thing as normal. Every childhood and family are different. As I keep saying, comparisons with other families and situations are deeply flawed and unhelpful.

So, when you worry your child is not having a normal experience, it is likely a misplaced fear. We hear of people having unhappy childhoods, and there is of course no doubt that some childhoods are happier, more fulfilling and more stable than others. But what makes a happy childhood? It is an elusive concept to define. It is not dependent, as I previously alluded to, upon wealth, privilege, number of parents, same-sex or not, etc. There are some basic requirements set down by the legally binding international agreement, the United Nations Convention on the Rights of the Child (UNCRC), such as non-discrimination and devotion to the best interests of the child. In non-war zones and developed countries, these needs and protections are largely met by society and family, with the exception perhaps of child abuse, an ongoing scourge within the UK.

Once the toddler phase is reached, everything seems to move so fast. They are becoming rapidly independent, with their own personalities, their likes and, more importantly (as this will raise the decibel levels to hearing-loss proportions), their dislikes.

Control (if any has been achieved by this point) can be very hard to maintain. Many activities of daily living can become battlegrounds. This is where parents must be supported to accept that they cannot win all the battles; they are lucky if they can win a few. It can be exhausting. But more importantly, it can be scary to see your child growing up and finding the control ebbing away.

Growing up is never easy. Children face a multitude of obstacles and challenges. School is probably the greatest. I touched on this briefly previously. The kind of bullying culture I experienced in my school life, which was truly horrendous, and shamefully contributed to by some of the teachers (particularly the sports ones as I have two left feet), is much less of a problem these days – overt bullying in school is largely not tolerated. However, the problem is now more subtle and, in some ways, harder to deal with, given that cyberbullying is now the most common form of bullying. It is hugely damaging to children's mental health, and you as parents may be oblivious to it. Your child will not be coming home with bruises or broken ribs, as I experienced, and you are not seeing what they are seeing on social media (a misnomer in so many ways, as it can be such an anti-social vehicle).

Parents really struggle with this aspect of their child's life, and I am frequently asked how they can manage this. The fundamental problem is loss of control, and the answer is not to remove your child's presence or access to social media as this will isolate and ostracize them even more.

You simply hope that by having as open and non-judgmental lines of communication with them as possible, they will reach out for help when they need it. There are signs you can spot of anxiety and depression creeping in, which so frequently have their roots in school or their social circle. Gradual change in personality, increasing reservation and withdrawal, spending more and more time (including meal times) in their bedroom, irritability and talk-back. Of course, this may reflect the normal ravages of testosterone, etc., but gently showing that you are there to listen to whatever may be bothering them is crucial. One of the hardest things for all of us is trying to get a young adult to open up if they have shut down.

Letting your child go and gradually losing the control on their life is so hard. The bird has to fly the nest eventually, and all you can do is hope the nest was so comfy and safe they will willingly return often. Of course, if the food is good, and the washing machine able to get rid of the most unspeakable stains, then you are on to a winner. There is no guarantee of a close relationship with your child as they enter their teens and beyond, and sometimes despite doing absolutely everything possible to support and protect them, they head out into the world and don't maintain close contact. It can seem cruel. Having said that, just because they don't ring often, or visit, that does not mean they don't have an enduring deep love and bond with you.

What if it is just easier?

What is the worst that could
happen if you ...

Let them have that sweet?

Let them use an iPad at dinner?

Let them have a scooter?

Let them stay up past their bedtime?

Let them sleep in your bed once
or twice a week?

Let them run and run?

Let them be children?

Let them fall down?

Let them have ice cream for breakfast?

Let them spend some time with
someone other than you?

Let them fall out with a friend
and then make up?

Let them realize they can't be
good at everything?

Let them be bored?

Let them . . .

Would it be so bad?
Would the world implode?

It doesn't make you a bad mum, it doesn't mean you are lazy, it means you're picking your battles and making everyone's life easier and more enjoyable. Whoever started telling everyone that they had to do it all and enjoy every second of it clearly didn't have it all to do. Learn to delegate and take the help when it's offered, don't be too proud and accept your limits. Guess what? We all have them.

WHAT IF 'NO' ISN'T GOOD ENOUGH?

How many times have you said 'no' to your kids, with absolutely no response? Are you even a parent if the answer to that question is 'Never'?

There's nothing more frustrating than a child that won't take no for an answer and it's so easy to lose all sense of calm and patience. I find myself saying, 'Come on, we've had a really nice day, don't ruin it now.' Because kids totally understand that applied logic, right? No, I didn't think so either. It's usually when you're out and there's loads of people around when a tantrum happens, so that the maximum amount of people can watch the debate between you and your five-year-old unfold, which only means you have less patience and feel more embarrassed as it looks like you clearly have no authority when it comes to your child. That's what your paranoia and mother guilt tells you anyway. We've all been somewhere and not wanted to leave. The term 'FOMO' (fear of missing out) comes to mind. So why do we expect our kids to feel any differently?

I don't believe that there's a parent out there that's never been pushed to their absolute limits by their own child. And I'm sure we all deal with that moment differently – our breaking point. We've all had those days when we've dealt with it in the 'wrong' way, when we lose it and shout at our children. Very quickly followed by a flood of guilt. In those moments, I simply apologize once I've calmed down. Say sorry for shouting, that shouting is not a good thing, and let them know the reason why they didn't behave correctly and then give them a hug. I usually find that my kids have either moved on completely or have taken the time to realize that what they did was wrong and they apologize too. Not everything in life goes our way and sometimes we react to that badly and irrationally. I want our children to know that, if that happens, they need to take stock and address it later. In my eyes, it's a good lesson to learn. We can't always

I don't believe that there's a parent out there that's never been pushed to their absolute limits by their own child.

pefectly deal with situations in a highly stressful and pressurized moment. And that's something I try to teach my kids. That I don't expect them to be perfect either, nor should they expect to be. Reactions are part of being human, but learning is part of being a good human. I just want them to try their best and if they get it wrong, to pick themselves up, learn from that mistake and try again. This applies to both their school and home lives. But I often wonder why can't I tell myself the same thing? Probably because I've been taught for many years that is not good enough.

Once pushed to my limits, I always try to take a step back and think about why. Sometimes it really is that your child just won't listen. But maybe they're tired or having a bad day? If they're anything like mine, maybe they're hangry? Remember, they're human like us.

Maybe you're tired? Been burning the candle at both ends? Not taking enough time out for yourself? Forgotten to take your meds? Due on? Something at work or financial is stressing you out? There can be so many reasons. Because we're always juggling a million things at once.

WHAT IS MY BEST?

No one's version of their best is the same as someone else's, nor should it be.

I bet you always remember those days where everything went wrong and you use this is as a weapon to beat yourself up with whenever something happens to your children. You tell yourself how awful you are, how much you have failed them, how much they will hate you when they grow up. I bet you spend much more time thinking about this than the great days where everything went to plan and it all worked out just fine because of you. In fact, I bet you never remind yourself how great you are.

As a mum who suffers with depression and anxiety, the bad days are really bad.

If I'm having a day where all I want to do is cry or hide in my bed, I will beat myself up about that one day for weeks and weeks and it will be for ever embedded and labelled in my mind as *that* moment I FAILED MY KIDS. But these are the anomaly, not the everyday.

These are not normal days but they do form part of my normal. I have to accept that I haven't failed my kids, I am just me, and I give them so much love that they would never doubt my care and belief and love in them.

The truth is, my kids have helped me massively with my mental health and they were the sole reason I wanted to get as well as I could, before they were even born, because I wanted to be a good mother.

They've also taught me to enjoy the smaller things in life and that as hard as I might try:

I am never going to be perfect
(AND NEITHER IS ANYONE ELSE).
I cannot control everything that
happens (AND NEITHER CAN
ANYONE ELSE).

I understand that my anxiety is a
part of me and that it lives in me
and that is who I am.

It doesn't mean that I am a terrible mother or that I am not doing a good job. And I want you to know that too. When you feel sad or down, don't feel as though you are alone or that what you are experiencing is an abnormal feeling. This is what it is like being a mother.

We have to learn not to be so hard on ourselves. We've been told so many times that we have to be perfect and only we can change the narrative. Who decides what's perfect anyway? I'm sure my idea of a perfect mother is very different from yours, and so it should be. And the one thing I have learned, and I hope you do too, is that perfect is a useless model that sets you up to fail and means you will forever be racked with mother's guilt or a sense of not living up to this important role. Remember perfect isn't reality. What really matters is that you find a way to be you while supporting your children in all the strange and beautiful ways they will need you over the years. Don't make them feel as though perfect is something they have to live up to and become. Let them understand all they need to be is themselves – leading by example.

WHAT IF I NEED HELP?

My depression has improved mostly because I am not preoccupied by it and don't have time to think too much about it and am physically unable to spend too many days in bed crying. However, that's not always a good thing as it means things build up. I find that sometimes it all just catches up with me and becomes overwhelming. I do the exact opposite of what I know I should do and I often push through until I reach breaking point. Also, in the madness of family life, I often forget to reorder my antidepressants. You'd think after all this time I'd be organized, but I am not. This then results in me slipping deeper and deeper into a dark place. With the added bonus of withdrawal symptoms. By the time I receive my tablets, it takes nearly double the time to get my mood back up, which fills me with guilt, as I am not the best mum to be around.

The what ifs, the why is, the how to and the IS IT MEs

I want you to know that no question is too small or too big. That every mother has asked it before and will ask it again. The undertaking is huge and we can never understand till we have done it how much it will change us, our minds and our lives for ever. It is truly one of the strangest and most incredible jobs you will ever learn, and as with any job you will have to make mistakes and fail in order to really grow into the role and learn how you are best able to fulfill it. Remember, you and your family are all that matter and as long as everything you do is done with the best intentions, you can't go wrong. The more you open up and start these conversations with other mums, the more you'll realize this. If you thought of yourself and spoke to yourself in the same way that you talk to your friends or the mums on social media, imagine how much better you'd feel about yourself. Easier said than done, I know. I'll let you know when I start to manage it myself!

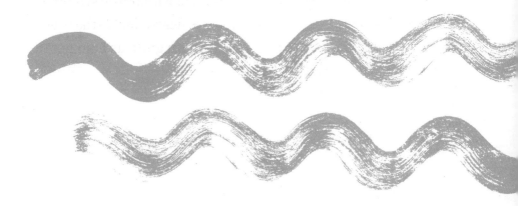

WHAT HAPPENS NEXT?

Remember there will come a time when your child or baby isn't small and they do become aware of you as a person too.

That you have failings and fears and faults and talents and shame and guilt, just like them.

The giant puzzle of things they have to figure out, you have had to do too.

You have had a life that they are about to experience and just like when big things happen to them and they grow up from it, so did you.

And there will come a time when they see you. They see past you as a mum or as a parent or as a carer.

And they see you.

Who do you want to be when they do?

That person who looks back at them needs not to have dissolved themselves fully into motherhood and lost themselves wholly along the way. The person that looks back at them needs to be you. A grown-up and slightly different person from who you probably are now. But it still needs to be you. So, when you feel as though you are holding onto yourself too much and you should give more of yourself to them, remember there will come a time when they expect to get to know you, not need you. And you deserve to still find time and care helping that person too.

AFTERWORD

And there was a time when I would imagine the people my boys would grow up into.

- What kind of attributes would they have?

- What sort of future lay ahead of them?

- Who would they be?

- What would they give to the world?

- Would they be industrious?

- Would they be ambitious?

- Who would they love?

- What would they do?

But as time goes on, I realize I just want them to be happy, good people. All the ideas of what their lives would be have gone.

I don't care what their lives look like, as long as life brings them joy and they are good people.

HELP AND SUPPORT

Mind

Helpline: 0300 123 3393
info@mind.org.uk
mind.org.uk

Mind's helplines provide information and support by phone and email for anyone experiencing a mental health problem. On Mind's website, you can also find information about difficulties you may face as a parent with a mental health problem, details of the support available and suggestions on how to help yourself and your children. To find out more about parenting with a mental health problem, go to www.mind.org.uk/information-support/tips-for-everyday-living

Action for Children

actionforchildren.org.uk

The Parent Talk section of the Action for Children website (parents.actionforchildren.org.uk) offers down-to-earth parenting advice. You can browse articles on the most common parenting questions from their experts or talk one-to-one with a qualified parenting coach about anything that's worrying you. It's free, and no topic is too big, small, or embarrassing.

Family Lives

familylives.org.uk
Helpline: 0808 800 2222

Family Lives was formed over forty years ago by volunteers, with the aim of ensuring that all parents had somewhere to turn before they reached crisis point. Family Lives provides targeted early intervention and crisis support to families who are struggling with issues including family breakdown, challenging relationships and behaviour, debt, and emotional and mental wellbeing.

ParentLine Scotland

Helpline: 08000 28 22 33
parentlinescotland.org.uk

If you live in Scotland, you can call the helpline set up by Children 1st, Scotland's National Children's Charity, for practical advice and support. Calls are free.

Home-Start

home-start.org.uk

Home-Start is a local community network of trained volunteers and expert support helping families with young children. Home-Start supports parents as they learn to cope, improve their confidence and build better lives for their children from birth to starting school. Parents struggling with post-natal depression, isolation, physical health problems, bereavement and many other issues receive the support of a volunteer who will spend around two hours a week in a family's home supporting them in the ways they need.

ERIC

Helpline: 0808 169 9949
eric.org.uk

ERIC is a charity dedicated to helping children manage and overcome continence conditions. Potty- and toilet training can be stressful and challenging for the whole family, and ERIC offers reliable advice about what to do when things go wrong. ERIC's potty-training guide is available to download at www.eric.org.uk/guide-to-potty-training

This **brazen** book was created by

Publishing Director: Romilly Morgan
Senior Editor: Alex Stetter
Assistant Editor: Sarah Kyle
Deputy Art Director: Jaz Bahra
Cover illustrator: Tatiana Boyko
Illustrator: Ella Mclean
Copyeditor: Sarah Hulbert
Typesetter: Jeremy Tilston
Senior Production Manager: Peter Hunt
Sales: Marianne Laidlaw, Kevin Hawkins, Stuart Lemon
Publicity & Marketing: Caroline Brown, Matt Grindon, Megan Brown
Legal: Sasha Duszynska Lewis, Imogen Plouviez